GLUTEN-FREE DIET & RECIPES COOKBOOK

Essential Guide for Beginners, Shopping Guide, 7-Day
Meal Plan for a Gluten-Free Lifestyle

Asher Greenfield

Disclaimer Notice:

The author and publishers have endeavored to ensure the accuracy and timeliness of the information provided in this book. However, medical understanding evolves constantly, and new research may alter perspectives on health and nutrition. Therefore, the author and publishers cannot guarantee the accuracy, completeness, or timeliness of the information presented herein.

The Gluten-Free Diet discussed in this book is a dietary approach that may offer potential health benefits, but its suitability may vary among individuals. It is essential to consult a healthcare professional before making significant dietary changes, especially if you have underlying health conditions, allergies, or are taking medications.

The author and publishers disclaim any responsibility for adverse effects or consequences resulting from the use or application of the information contained in this book. The reader assumes full responsibility for their health and dietary decisions, and the author and publishers are not liable for any direct or indirect damages or losses that may arise.

Table of Contents

Chapter 1: Introduction to Gluten-Free Diet

Understanding Gluten

Gluten is a protein found in certain grains like wheat, barley, and rye. It acts as a binding agent, giving elasticity to dough and helping it rise during baking. While gluten is harmless for most people, it can cause serious health issues for those with gluten-related disorders, such as celiac disease, wheat allergy, or non-celiac gluten sensitivity.

Celiac Disease: This autoimmune disorder affects about 1% of the population worldwide. In individuals with celiac disease, consuming gluten triggers an immune response that damages the small intestine, leading to various symptoms such as abdominal pain, diarrhea, fatigue, and nutrient deficiencies.

Wheat Allergy: Unlike celiac disease, wheat allergy is an immune reaction to proteins found specifically in wheat. Symptoms can range from mild to severe and may include hives, difficulty breathing, and anaphylaxis. It's important to note that wheat allergy is different from gluten intolerance or sensitivity.

Non-Celiac Gluten Sensitivity: Some individuals experience adverse reactions to gluten without having celiac disease or wheat allergy. This condition is known as non-celiac gluten sensitivity. Symptoms can include gastrointestinal issues, headaches, fatigue, and joint pain. Although the mechanisms behind non-celiac gluten sensitivity are not fully understood, avoiding gluten often alleviates symptoms in affected individuals.

Understanding gluten and its effects on the body is crucial for anyone considering adopting a gluten-free diet. By recognizing the role of gluten in various health conditions, individuals can make informed decisions about their dietary choices and take proactive steps to manage their health effectively.

Benefits of a Gluten-Free Diet

Transitioning to a gluten-free diet can offer several potential benefits, particularly for individuals with gluten-related disorders. While the primary reason for following a gluten-free diet is to manage these conditions, there are additional advantages that may be experienced:

Relief from Digestive Discomfort: For individuals with celiac disease or non-celiac gluten sensitivity, eliminating gluten from the diet can alleviate symptoms such as bloating, gas, diarrhea, and abdominal pain. By avoiding gluten-containing foods, the inflammation and damage to the digestive system can be reduced, leading to improved overall digestive health.

Improved Nutrient Absorption: In individuals with celiac disease, the inflammation in the small intestine can impair the absorption of nutrients from food. Adopting a gluten-free diet allows the intestinal lining to heal, enhancing the body's ability to absorb essential vitamins and minerals, such as iron, calcium, and vitamin D.

Increased Energy Levels: Some people report feeling more energetic and less fatigued after eliminating gluten from their diets. This may be attributed to better digestion, improved nutrient absorption, and reduced inflammation in the body.

Potential Weight Loss: While a gluten-free diet is not inherently a weight-loss diet, some individuals may experience weight loss as a result of eliminating certain processed foods and refined carbohydrates that contain gluten. However, it's essential to make healthy food choices and maintain a balanced diet to achieve sustainable weight loss.

Enhanced Mental Clarity: Brain fog and cognitive difficulties are common symptoms associated with gluten-related disorders. By following a gluten-free diet, individuals may experience improved mental clarity, concentration, and overall cognitive function.

Support for Other Health Conditions: Some individuals with autoimmune disorders or chronic inflammatory conditions may find that reducing or eliminating gluten from their diets helps manage their symptoms and improve their overall health.

Exploration of New Foods: Embracing a gluten-free diet can encourage individuals to explore a wider variety of whole, naturally gluten-free foods such as fruits, vegetables, lean proteins, legumes, nuts, and seeds. This can lead to a more diverse and nutritious diet overall.

While there are potential benefits to adopting a gluten-free diet, it's essential to approach dietary changes with caution and seek guidance from healthcare professionals, especially for those without diagnosed gluten-related disorders. Consulting with a registered dietitian or nutritionist can help ensure that nutritional needs are met while following a gluten-free lifestyle.

Who Should Follow a Gluten-Free Diet

A gluten-free diet is primarily recommended for individuals diagnosed with gluten-related disorders, including celiac disease, wheat allergy, and non-celiac gluten sensitivity. However, there are specific groups of people who may benefit from or need to consider adopting a gluten-free diet:

Individuals with Celiac Disease: Celiac disease is an autoimmune disorder triggered by the ingestion of gluten. If you've been diagnosed with celiac disease through blood tests and intestinal biopsies, following a strict gluten-free diet is essential to manage symptoms, promote intestinal healing, and prevent long-term complications.

Those with Wheat Allergy: Individuals with a confirmed wheat allergy should avoid consuming wheat-containing foods to prevent allergic reactions, which can range from mild to severe. While wheat is not the only source of gluten, many gluten-free products are also wheat-free, making a gluten-free diet suitable for individuals with this allergy.

People with Non-Celiac Gluten Sensitivity: Non-celiac gluten sensitivity (NCGS) is characterized by adverse reactions to gluten in individuals without celiac disease or wheat allergy. While the mechanisms of NCGS are not fully understood, symptoms such as gastrointestinal discomfort, fatigue, and headaches may improve with a gluten-free diet.

Individuals with Dermatitis Herpetiformis: Dermatitis herpetiformis is a skin manifestation of celiac disease, characterized by itchy, blistering skin rashes. Following a gluten-free diet can help manage symptoms and prevent flare-ups of this condition.

Those at Risk for Celiac Disease: If you have a family history of celiac disease or are at risk for the condition due to certain genetic factors, your healthcare provider may recommend periodic screening for celiac disease and possibly adopting a gluten-free diet, even if you haven't experienced symptoms.

People with Other Autoimmune Disorders: Some individuals with autoimmune disorders such as rheumatoid arthritis, lupus, or Hashimoto's thyroiditis may find that reducing gluten intake helps manage symptoms and inflammation. While the evidence is limited, a trial of a gluten-free diet under the guidance of a healthcare provider may be considered.

Individuals with Chronic Digestive Issues: If you experience chronic digestive issues such as irritable bowel syndrome (IBS) and have not found relief with other dietary interventions, you may benefit from trying a gluten-free diet to determine if gluten is a trigger for your symptoms.

It's important to note that adopting a gluten-free diet without a medical necessity can pose challenges, including potential nutrient deficiencies and reliance on processed gluten-free products.

Getting Started

Embarking on a gluten-free diet can seem daunting at first, but with the right knowledge and resources, it can become a manageable and rewarding lifestyle choice. Here are some essential steps to help you get started on your gluten-free journey:

Educate Yourself: Understanding what gluten is and where it hides in foods is crucial for success on a gluten-free diet. Learn to read food labels carefully, as gluten can be present in unexpected places such as sauces, seasonings, and processed foods. Familiarize yourself with naturally gluten-free grains and ingredients to expand your culinary options.

Clean Out Your Pantry: Take inventory of your pantry and remove any foods containing gluten, including wheat flour, barley, rye, and products derived from these grains. Donate unopened items to food banks or local charities, and consider replacing staple items with gluten-free alternatives.

Stock Up on Gluten-Free Staples: Build a pantry stocked with gluten-free essentials to support your new dietary lifestyle. This may include gluten-free flours (such as rice flour, almond flour, or coconut flour), gluten-free pasta, whole grains (like quinoa, buckwheat, and millet), gluten-free oats, and baking ingredients such as xanthan gum and baking powder.

Explore Naturally Gluten-Free Foods: Focus on incorporating whole, naturally gluten-free foods into your diet, such as fruits, vegetables, lean proteins, dairy products, nuts, seeds, and legumes. These foods are not only nutritious but also naturally free of gluten, making them safe options for your meals and snacks.

Experiment with Gluten-Free Recipes: There are countless delicious gluten-free recipes available online, in cookbooks, and through cooking blogs. Start experimenting with gluten-free versions of your favorite dishes, from pasta and pizza to baked goods and desserts. Cooking at home allows you to have full control over the ingredients and ensures a safe, gluten-free meal.

Be Mindful of Cross-Contamination: Preventing cross-contamination is essential when following a gluten-free diet. Use separate utensils, cutting boards, and kitchen equipment for gluten-free and gluten-containing foods. Clean surfaces thoroughly before preparing gluten-free meals, and be cautious when dining out to avoid potential cross-contact with gluten.

Seek Support and Guidance: Transitioning to a gluten-free diet may come with challenges, but you're not alone. Connect with support groups, online communities, and forums where you can share experiences, ask questions, and find encouragement from others following a gluten-free lifestyle. Additionally, consider consulting with a registered dietitian or nutritionist specializing in gluten-free diets for personalized guidance and support.

Remember that adopting a gluten-free diet is a journey, and it's okay to take it one step at a time. With patience, persistence, and a positive attitude, you can successfully navigate the gluten-free lifestyle and enjoy the benefits of improved health and well-being.

Chapter 2: Gluten-Free Shopping Guide

Identifying Gluten-Containing Foods

Successfully navigating a gluten-free lifestyle begins with being able to identify foods that contain gluten. While some sources of gluten are obvious, others may be less apparent. Here are key tips for identifying gluten-containing foods:

Read Food Labels: When grocery shopping, carefully read the ingredient labels of packaged foods. Look for common gluten-containing ingredients such as wheat, barley, rye, and their derivatives. Keep in mind that gluten can hide under various names, including:

- **Wheat-based ingredients:** wheat flour, wheat starch, wheat germ, semolina, durum, farina, bulgur, and spelt.
- **Barley-derived ingredients:** barley malt, malt extract, malt flavoring, malt vinegar, and barley malt syrup.
- **Rye ingredients:** rye flour and rye bread.
- **Other less common sources:** triticale (a hybrid of wheat and rye), couscous, seitan, and some soy sauces.

Be Cautious of Processed Foods: Processed and packaged foods often contain hidden gluten in the form of additives, thickeners, and flavorings. Check labels for ingredients like modified food starch, hydrolyzed vegetable protein (HVP), and maltodextrin, as they may be derived from gluten-containing grains.

Avoid Certain Food Categories: Many foods inherently contain gluten and should be avoided on a gluten-free diet. These include:

- Breads, pastas, and baked goods made with wheat flour.
- Cereals containing wheat, barley, or rye.
- Beer and malt beverages.
- Some sauces and condiments, such as soy sauce, teriyaki sauce, and certain gravies.
- Processed meats that may contain fillers or breadcrumbs.

Use Gluten-Free Certification Labels: Look for products labeled as "gluten-free" or certified gluten-free by reputable organizations. These labels indicate that the product has undergone testing to ensure it meets gluten-free standards and is safe for consumption by individuals with gluten-related disorders.

Be Mindful of Cross-Contamination: Even if a food product is naturally gluten-free, it can become contaminated with gluten during processing or preparation. Be cautious when purchasing foods from shared production facilities or when dining out, and look for products labeled with statements such as "processed in a facility that also processes wheat" or "may contain traces of wheat."

Ask Questions: When in doubt about the gluten content of a particular food item, don't hesitate to ask questions. Whether you're dining out at a restaurant or shopping at a grocery store, seek clarification from staff or manufacturers to ensure that the food is safe for your gluten-free diet.

By familiarizing yourself with common sources of gluten and practicing diligent label reading, you can confidently identify gluten-containing foods and make informed choices to support your gluten-free lifestyle.

Gluten-Free Alternatives

Transitioning to a gluten-free diet doesn't mean giving up your favorite foods; it simply requires finding suitable alternatives that are free from gluten-containing grains. Fortunately, there are numerous gluten-free alternatives available to replace traditional wheat-based products. Here are some popular options to consider:

Flours and Grains: Replace wheat flour with gluten-free alternatives to make baked goods, bread, and other flour-based recipes. Common gluten-free flours and grains include:

- Rice flour (white or brown)
- Almond flour
- Coconut flour
- Sorghum flour
- Buckwheat flour
- Quinoa flour
- Cornmeal
- Millet
- Amaranth
- Teff

Gluten-Free Pasta: Enjoy pasta dishes without gluten by opting for gluten-free pasta made from alternative flours such as rice, quinoa, corn, chickpea, or lentil. These varieties offer similar taste and texture to traditional pasta and are available in various shapes and sizes.

Breads and Wraps: Gluten-free bread and wraps are widely available in grocery stores and bakeries. Look for options made with gluten-free grains, seeds, or nut flours to enjoy sandwiches, toast, and wraps without gluten.

Baking Mixes and Prepared Foods: Many companies offer gluten-free baking mixes and prepared foods to simplify meal preparation. From pancake mixes and cake mixes to pizza dough and cookie dough, these convenient options allow you to indulge in your favorite treats without gluten.

Gluten-Free Oats: While oats are naturally gluten-free, they may be cross-contaminated with gluten during processing. Look for certified gluten-free oats to ensure they're safe for your gluten-free diet. Use gluten-free oats to make oatmeal, granola, cookies, and other baked goods.

Flavor Enhancers: Some ingredients commonly used to add flavor to dishes may contain gluten. Opt for gluten-free alternatives such as tamari or gluten-free soy sauce instead of traditional soy sauce, and choose gluten-free Worcestershire sauce, bouillon cubes, and condiments to season your meals.

Thickening Agents: Substitute wheat-based thickeners like flour or roux with gluten-free alternatives such as cornstarch, arrowroot powder, tapioca starch, or potato starch to thicken sauces, gravies, and soups.

Snacks and Sweets: Indulge in gluten-free snacks and sweets to satisfy your cravings without gluten.

Look for options like gluten-free crackers, chips, popcorn, chocolate, candies, and snack bars made with gluten-free ingredients.

By incorporating these gluten-free alternatives into your shopping list and pantry staples, you can continue to enjoy a diverse and flavorful diet while adhering to your gluten-free lifestyle. Experiment with different options to find your favorite gluten-free substitutes and discover new culinary possibilities along the way.

Stocking Your Pantry

Building a well-stocked pantry is essential for maintaining a gluten-free diet and ensuring you have the necessary ingredients to prepare delicious and satisfying meals. Here's a guide to stocking your pantry with gluten-free essentials:

Gluten-Free Flours: Replace wheat flour with a variety of gluten-free flours to accommodate different recipes and cooking needs. Stock up on versatile options such as rice flour, almond flour, coconut flour, and gluten-free all-purpose flour blends.

Whole Grains and Legumes: Incorporate a variety of whole grains and legumes into your pantry to add nutrition and diversity to your meals. Choose gluten-free grains like quinoa, brown rice, millet, buckwheat, and certified gluten-free oats, along with legumes such as lentils, beans, and chickpeas.

Gluten-Free Pasta and Noodles: Keep your pantry stocked with gluten-free pasta and noodles made from alternative grains like rice, corn, quinoa, or lentils. Having these options on hand allows you to whip up quick and satisfying pasta dishes without gluten.

Canned and Jarred Goods: Opt for canned and jarred goods that are labeled gluten-free or naturally free from gluten-containing ingredients. This includes items like canned beans, tomatoes, vegetables, salsa, pasta sauce, broth, pickles, olives, and nut butters.

Baking Essentials: Ensure you have essential baking ingredients for making gluten-free treats and baked goods. Stock up on gluten-free baking powder, baking soda, vanilla extract, cocoa powder, chocolate chips, and other gluten-free flavorings and extracts.

Condiments and Sauces: Check labels carefully to find gluten-free versions of your favorite condiments and sauces, such as ketchup, mustard, mayonnaise, salad dressings, barbecue sauce, salsa, tamari or gluten-free soy sauce, and Worcestershire sauce.

Snacks and Crackers: Keep a selection of gluten-free snacks and crackers on hand for quick and convenient munching. Look for gluten-free crackers, rice cakes, popcorn, nuts, dried fruits, gluten-free granola bars, and gluten-free snack mixes.

Nut and Seed Butters: Nut and seed butters are versatile pantry staples that can be used as spreads, toppings, or ingredients in recipes. Choose natural varieties of peanut butter, almond butter, cashew butter, sunflower seed butter, and tahini that are free from gluten-containing additives.

Gluten-Free Mixes and Convenience Foods: While it's essential to focus on whole, minimally processed foods, having some gluten-free mixes and convenience foods on hand can be convenient for busy days. Consider stocking up on gluten-free pancake mixes, baking mixes, frozen meals, and pre-packaged snacks.

Herbs, Spices, and Seasonings: Enhance the flavor of your gluten-free dishes with a variety of herbs, spices, and seasonings. Keep a well-stocked spice rack with gluten-free options like salt, pepper, garlic powder, onion powder, cumin, paprika, oregano, basil, and curry powder.

By stocking your pantry with these gluten-free essentials, you'll be well-prepared to create flavorful, nutritious meals and snacks while adhering to your gluten-free lifestyle. Regularly check labels and be vigilant about cross-contamination to ensure that all items in your pantry are safe for consumption.

Sample Shopping List

Creating a comprehensive shopping list is essential for maintaining a well-rounded gluten-free diet and ensuring you have all the necessary ingredients on hand for your meals and snacks. Here's a sample shopping list to guide you during your next grocery trip:

Produce:

- Fresh fruits (e.g., apples, bananas, berries, oranges)
- Fresh vegetables (e.g., leafy greens, tomatoes, cucumbers, bell peppers)
- Potatoes (white, sweet)
- Onions
- Garlic
- Avocados

Grains and Cereals:

- Brown rice
- Quinoa
- Certified gluten-free oats
- Cornmeal
- Gluten-free pasta (e.g., rice pasta, quinoa pasta)
- Rice noodles

Flours and Baking Ingredients:

- Gluten-free all-purpose flour blend
- Almond flour
- Coconut flour

- Gluten-free baking powder
- Baking soda
- Vanilla extract

Canned and Jarred Goods:

- Canned beans (e.g., black beans, chickpeas)
- Canned tomatoes
- Tomato paste
- Vegetable or chicken broth (gluten-free)
- Pickles
- Olives
- Salsa

Dairy and Dairy Alternatives:

- Milk (dairy or non-dairy)
- Yogurt (dairy or non-dairy)
- Cheese (check for gluten-free varieties)
- Butter or margarine (check for gluten-free options)
- Almond milk, coconut milk, or soy milk

Proteins:

- Eggs
- Lean cuts of meat (e.g., chicken breast, turkey, lean beef)
- Fish (fresh or frozen)
- Tofu or tempeh
- Canned tuna or salmon

Snacks and Convenience Foods:

- Gluten-free crackers
- Rice cakes
- Popcorn
- Nuts and seeds
- Gluten-free granola bars
- Dried fruits

Condiments and Sauces:

- Gluten-free soy sauce or tamari
- Gluten-free pasta sauce
- Mustard

- Mayonnaise
- Olive oil
- Vinegar (e.g., balsamic, apple cider)

Herbs, Spices, and Seasonings:

- Salt
- Pepper
- Garlic powder
- Onion powder
- Paprika
- Cumin
- Oregano
- Basil

Miscellaneous:

- Gluten-free pancake mix
- Gluten-free bread or wraps
- Nut butters (e.g., peanut butter, almond butter)
- Gluten-free cereal

Remember to check labels carefully to ensure that all products are labeled as gluten-free or do not contain any gluten-containing ingredients. Additionally, consider purchasing certified gluten-free products when available to minimize the risk of cross-contamination. With a well-planned shopping list, you can confidently navigate the grocery store and stock your kitchen with gluten-free essentials to support your dietary needs.

Chapter 3: Meal Planning on a Gluten-Free

Importance of Meal Planning

Meal planning is a crucial aspect of successfully navigating a gluten-free diet. Whether you're managing celiac disease, gluten sensitivity, or simply choosing to avoid gluten for health reasons, thoughtful meal planning can help you stay on track and ensure that your dietary needs are met. Here's why meal planning is essential for individuals following a gluten-free lifestyle:

Ensures Gluten-Free Options: Planning your meals in advance allows you to carefully select gluten-free ingredients and recipes, reducing the risk of accidentally consuming gluten. By thoughtfully choosing gluten-free alternatives and incorporating naturally gluten-free foods into your meals, you can create a varied and satisfying menu that meets your nutritional needs.

Saves Time and Effort: Meal planning saves time and reduces stress by streamlining the cooking process. By deciding what to prepare ahead of time, you can efficiently shop for ingredients, minimize food waste, and avoid last-minute trips to the grocery store. Additionally, batch cooking and meal prepping on designated days can save time during busy weekdays and ensure that you have convenient, gluten-free options readily available.

Promotes Balanced Nutrition: Planning your meals allows you to create balanced, nutrient-rich dishes that support your overall health and well-being. By including a variety of fruits, vegetables, whole grains, lean proteins, and healthy fats in your meal plan, you can ensure that you're meeting your nutritional requirements while avoiding gluten-containing grains.

Prevents Cross-Contamination: Meal planning enables you to control your food preparation environment and minimize the risk of cross-contamination with gluten. By designating gluten-free cooking utensils, cutting boards, and cooking surfaces, you can create a safe kitchen environment where gluten-free meals can be prepared without the risk of contamination.

Facilitates Dining Out: Planning your meals in advance can help you navigate dining-out situations more effectively. By researching gluten-free options at restaurants or packing gluten-free snacks and meals when traveling, you can ensure that you have safe and satisfying dining experiences outside of your home.

Supports Budgeting and Cost-Effectiveness: Meal planning allows you to budget effectively and minimize food waste by purchasing only the ingredients you need for your planned meals. By buying in bulk, taking advantage of sales, and repurposing leftovers, you can save money while maintaining a gluten-free diet.

Empowers Personalization and Variety: Meal planning gives you the flexibility to personalize your meals according to your preferences, dietary restrictions, and nutritional goals. Whether you're following a specific dietary plan or experimenting with new recipes, meal planning allows you to incorporate variety and creativity into your gluten-free menu.

In summary, meal planning plays a vital role in supporting a successful gluten-free lifestyle by ensuring access to safe, nutritious, and satisfying meals. By taking the time to plan and prepare your meals thoughtfully, you can enjoy the benefits of improved health, reduced stress, and greater confidence in managing your gluten-free diet.

Building Balanced Meals

Creating balanced meals is essential for maintaining optimal health and well-being on a gluten-free diet. By incorporating a variety of nutrient-rich foods into your meals, you can ensure that you're meeting your nutritional needs while enjoying delicious and satisfying dishes. Here's how to build balanced meals on a gluten-free diet:

Include Gluten-Free Grains and Starches: Start by choosing a gluten-free grain or starchy vegetable as the foundation of your meal. Options include:

- Brown rice
- Quinoa
- Buckwheat
- Millet
- Amaranth
- Sweet potatoes
- Corn

Add Lean Proteins: Incorporate lean sources of protein to provide satiety and support muscle health. Opt for gluten-free protein options such as:

- Skinless poultry (chicken, turkey)
- Lean cuts of beef or pork
- Fish and seafood
- Tofu or tempeh
- Legumes (beans, lentils)

Include Plenty of Vegetables: Load your plate with a colorful array of vegetables to add vitamins, minerals, fiber, and antioxidants to your meal. Aim to include a mix of leafy greens, cruciferous vegetables, root vegetables, and other non-starchy options such as:

- Spinach
- Kale
- Broccoli
- Cauliflower
- Bell peppers
- Carrots
- Zucchini
- Eggplant
- Mushrooms
- Tomatoes

Incorporate Healthy Fats: Don't forget to include healthy fats in your meals to support heart health and provide essential fatty acids. Add sources of healthy fats such as:

- Avocado
- Nuts and seeds (almonds, walnuts, chia seeds, flaxseeds)
- Olive oil
- Coconut oil
- Nut butters (peanut butter, almond butter)

Don't Forget about Fruit: Incorporate fresh or frozen fruits into your meals or enjoy them as snacks to add natural sweetness and additional vitamins and fiber to your diet. Choose a variety of fruits such as:

- Berries (strawberries, blueberries, raspberries)
- Apples
- Bananas
- Oranges
- Pineapple
- Mango
- Kiwi
- Grapes

Season with Herbs and Spices: Enhance the flavor of your meals with herbs, spices, and seasonings instead of relying on excess salt or processed sauces.

Stay Hydrated: Remember to stay hydrated by drinking plenty of water throughout the day. You can also enjoy herbal teas, infused water, or coconut water for added hydration and flavor.

Tips for Eating Out

Eating out can be challenging when following a gluten-free diet, as it requires navigating menus, communicating with restaurant staff, and ensuring that your meal is prepared safely to avoid gluten cross-contamination. However, with the right strategies and preparation, you can enjoy dining out while staying gluten-free. Here are some tips to help you dine out successfully:

Research Restaurants in Advance: Before choosing a restaurant, research their menu options and gluten-free offerings online. Look for restaurants that clearly label gluten-free items on their menu or offer customizable options that can be made gluten-free.

Call Ahead: If you're unsure about a restaurant's gluten-free options, call ahead to inquire about their gluten-free menu or accommodations for gluten-free diners. Speaking directly with the restaurant staff can help clarify any questions or concerns you may have about gluten cross-contamination or ingredient substitutions.

Ask Questions: When dining out, don't hesitate to ask questions about menu items, ingredients, and food preparation methods. Inquire about how dishes are prepared, whether gluten-containing ingredients are used, and if any cross-contamination risks exist in the kitchen.

Communicate Your Needs: Clearly communicate your dietary needs to your server or the restaurant staff. Explain that you have a gluten allergy or intolerance and request that your meal be prepared separately from gluten-containing dishes to prevent cross-contact.

Be Cautious of Hidden Gluten: Be vigilant about hidden sources of gluten in restaurant dishes, such as sauces, marinades, dressings, and seasonings. Ask for gluten-free alternatives or request that these items be omitted from your meal to avoid gluten exposure.

Choose Simple, Naturally Gluten-Free Options: Opt for dishes that are naturally gluten-free or easily customizable, such as salads, grilled meats or fish, steamed vegetables, and rice-based dishes. These options are less likely to contain hidden gluten and can be safer choices when dining out.

Avoid Shared Fryers: Be cautious when ordering fried foods, as they may be cooked in shared fryers with gluten-containing items, increasing the risk of cross-contamination. Ask if the restaurant has a dedicated gluten-free fryer or choose alternative cooking methods like grilling or baking.

Bring Your Own Gluten-Free Snacks: In case gluten-free options are limited or unavailable, consider bringing along gluten-free snacks or emergency food items to enjoy during your outing. This ensures that you have safe and satisfying options to fall back on if needed.

Express Gratitude and Provide Feedback: When dining out gluten-free, express appreciation to the restaurant staff for accommodating your dietary needs. Providing positive feedback encourages restaurants to continue offering gluten-free options and improves the dining experience for gluten-sensitive individuals.

By following these tips and being proactive about your dietary needs, you can enjoy dining out while staying safe and gluten-free. With practice and experience, you'll become more confident navigating restaurant menus and making informed choices that support your gluten-free lifestyle.

Meal Prep Ideas

Meal prepping is a time-saving strategy that involves preparing and portioning meals ahead of time, making it easier to maintain a gluten-free diet throughout the week. By dedicating a few hours to meal prep each week, you can ensure that you have nutritious and convenient gluten-free meals readily available. Here are some meal prep ideas to help you get started:

Batch Cooking Gluten-Free Staples: Prepare large batches of gluten-free grains, proteins, and vegetables to use as building blocks for multiple meals throughout the week. Cook quinoa, brown rice, or gluten-free pasta in bulk and portion them into individual containers for easy meal assembly.

Pre-Chopped Vegetables and Fruits: Wash, peel, and chop a variety of vegetables and fruits in advance to streamline meal preparation. Store pre-chopped produce in airtight containers or resealable bags in the refrigerator for quick and easy access when cooking or snacking.

Marinate and Pre-Cook Proteins: Marinate chicken, fish, tofu, or tempeh in your favorite gluten-free sauces or seasonings and pre-cook them for faster meal assembly. Grill, bake, or sauté proteins until cooked through, then portion them into containers for use in salads, stir-fries, or grain bowls.

Prepare Salad Ingredients: Create DIY salad kits by washing and chopping salad greens, vegetables, and toppings such as nuts, seeds, and cheese. Store each component separately in containers or resealable bags, then assemble your salads just before eating for maximum freshness.

Make Gluten-Free Sauces and Dressings: Whip up homemade gluten-free sauces, dressings, and condiments to enhance the flavor of your meals. Prepare batches of marinara sauce, pesto, vinaigrettes, and salsa to use as flavor-packed toppings or dipping sauces throughout the week.

Portion Snacks and Treats: Divide gluten-free snacks and treats into portion-controlled servings to prevent overeating and ensure that you always have gluten-free options on hand. Portion nuts, dried fruits, popcorn, gluten-free crackers, and homemade baked goods into individual bags or containers for convenient snacking.

Freeze Meals for Later: Prepare freezer-friendly meals in advance and store them in portion-sized containers for future use. Soups, stews, casseroles, and pasta dishes can all be batch-cooked and frozen for quick and easy meals on busy days.

Label and Date Containers: To stay organized, label each container with the contents and date of preparation before storing them in the refrigerator or freezer. This helps you keep track of what's inside and ensures that you use meals before they expire.

By incorporating these meal prep ideas into your routine, you can save time, reduce stress, and maintain a gluten-free diet with ease. Experiment with different recipes, ingredients, and cooking methods to customize your meal prep to suit your tastes and dietary preferences. With practice, meal prepping will become a valuable tool for staying on track with your gluten-free lifestyle.

Chapter 4: Gluten-Free 7 Day Meal Plan

Note: This meal plan is a sample and can be adjusted based on your dietary preferences, restrictions, and portion sizes. The calorie count is approximate for one serving.

Monday

Breakfast: Quinoa Porridge

Cook Time: 7 min | Prep Time: 5 min | Calories: Approximately 380 kcal	
Ingredients	**Directions**
<ul><li>2/3 cup (120g) quinoa flakes</li><li>1 cup (240ml) milk (use dairy-free milk for vegan option)</li><li>30g pistachios, chopped</li><li>1/2 cup (75g) blueberries</li><li>Coconut flakes, for topping</li></ul>	<ul><li>In a small saucepan, combine the quinoa flakes and milk.</li><li>Place the saucepan over medium heat and bring the mixture to a gentle simmer, stirring occasionally to prevent sticking. Reduce heat to low and continue to simmer for about 5-7 minutes, or until the porridge thickens to your desired consistency.</li><li>Once the porridge reaches your preferred thickness, remove it from the heat and transfer it to a serving bowl.</li><li>Top the quinoa porridge with chopped pistachios, blueberries, and a sprinkle of coconut flakes.</li></ul>

Lunch: Baked Beans, Spinach & Tomato on Toast

Cook Time: 10 min | Prep Time: 5 min | Calories: Approximately 420 kcal	
Ingredients	**Directions**
<ul><li>2 slices gluten-free bread</li><li>1 teaspoon spread (butter or dairy-free spread)</li><li>1 cup (240g) canned baked beans</li><li>1 cup (30g) fresh spinach leaves</li><li>1 tomato, sliced</li><li>Salt and pepper, to taste</li></ul>	<ul><li>Preheat your oven to 350°F (180°C).</li><li>Place the gluten-free bread slices on a baking sheet and toast them in the oven for about 5-7 minutes, or until they are crispy.</li><li>Meanwhile, in a small saucepan, heat the baked beans over medium heat until they are heated through, stirring occasionally.</li><li>While the beans are heating, steam the spinach leaves until they are wilted, either using a steamer basket or by placing them in a microwave-safe dish with a splash of water and microwaving for 1-2 minutes.</li><li>In a separate pan, grill the tomato slices over medium heat for 2-3 minutes on each side, until they are slightly charred.</li><li>Once everything is ready, spread the teaspoon of spread evenly over the toasted gluten-free bread slices.</li><li>Top each slice with half of the heated baked beans, followed by the steamed spinach and grilled tomato slices.</li><li>Season with salt and pepper to taste.</li></ul>

Dinner: Lentil & Feta Rice Salad

Cook Time: 20 min | Prep Time: 10 min | Calories: Approximately 450 kcal	
Ingredients	**Directions**
<ul><li>1 cup (200g) cooked lentils</li><li>Handful of crumbled feta cheese</li><li>2 teaspoons olive oil</li><li>1 cup (180g) cooked brown rice</li><li>1 cup (20g) torn rocket (arugula) leaves</li><li>2 tablespoons vinegar dressing</li><li>Chopped parsley, for garnish</li></ul>	<ul><li>Cook the brown rice and lentils according to package instructions. Once cooked, allow them to cool slightly.</li><li>In a large mixing bowl, combine the cooked lentils and brown rice.</li><li>Add the crumbled feta cheese and torn rocket leaves to the bowl.</li><li>Drizzle the olive oil over the salad ingredients and toss gently to combine.</li><li>Pour the vinegar dressing over the salad and toss again until everything is evenly coated.</li><li>Garnish the salad with chopped parsley.</li><li>Serve immediately, or refrigerate for a couple of hours to allow the flavors to meld together before serving.</li></ul>

Thursday

Breakfast: Strawberry Mango Smoothie

Cook Time: 0 min | Prep Time: 5 min | Calories: Approximately 250 kcal	
Ingredients	**Directions**
<ul><li>1 small mango, peeled and chopped</li><li>4 strawberries, hulled</li><li>1 cup (240ml) milk (use dairy-free milk for vegan option)</li><li>1/2 cup (120g) yogurt (use dairy-free yogurt for vegan option)</li><li>2 tablespoons linseed (flaxseed)</li><li>Rice puffs or rice flakes, for topping</li></ul>	<ul><li>Place the chopped mango, strawberries, milk, yogurt, and linseed in a blender.</li><li>Blend on high speed until smooth and creamy, about 1-2 minutes.</li><li>If the smoothie is too thick, add more milk to reach your desired consistency and blend again briefly.</li><li>Once the smoothie reaches the desired consistency, pour it into serving glasses.</li><li>Top each smoothie with a sprinkle of rice puffs or rice flakes for added crunch.</li></ul>

Lunch: Grilled Fish & Vegetables

Cook Time: 30 min	Prep Time: 15 min	Calories: Approximately 500 kcal	
Ingredients	**Directions**
<ul><li>2 fish fillets (such as cod, salmon, or tilapia), about 4-6 ounces (110-170g) each</li><li>Assorted vegetables for steaming (e.g., broccoli, carrots, bell peppers)</li><li>2 large potatoes</li><li>Olive oil</li><li>Salt and pepper, to taste</li><li>1 tub (150g) yogurt</li></ul>	<ul><li>Preheat your grill to medium-high heat.</li><li>Wash and scrub the potatoes thoroughly. Prick them with a fork a few times, then wrap each potato in foil.</li><li>Place the wrapped potatoes directly on the grill grates. Cook for about 25-30 minutes, turning occasionally, until they are tender when pierced with a fork.</li><li>While the potatoes are cooking, prepare the fish fillets. Brush them lightly with olive oil and season with salt and pepper on both sides.</li><li>Prepare the assorted vegetables for steaming by washing and cutting them into bite-sized pieces.</li><li>Once the potatoes have been on the grill for about 15 minutes, add the fish fillets to the grill. Grill the fish for about 4-5 minutes on each side, or until cooked through and flaky.</li><li>While the fish is grilling, steam the vegetables until they are tender-crisp, about 5-7 minutes.</li><li>Once everything is cooked, remove the potatoes, fish, and vegetables from the grill.</li><li>Serve the grilled fish alongside the steamed vegetables and a large baked or boiled potato. Drizzle the potato with a splash of olive oil.</li><li>Serve with a tub of yogurt on the side for added creaminess.</li></ul>

Dinner: Quinoa Tabbouleh With Sesame Eggs & Lamb

Cook Time: 20 min	Prep Time: 10 min	Calories: Approximately 550 kcal	
Ingredients	**Directions**
<ul><li>1/2 cup (90g) quinoa</li><li>1 cup (240ml) water</li><li>1 tablespoon olive oil</li><li>1 small onion, finely chopped</li><li>1 clove garlic, minced</li><li>1/2 cup (75g) cherry tomatoes, quartered</li><li>1/4 cup (15g) chopped fresh parsley</li><li>2 tablespoons (30ml) lemon juice</li><li>Salt and pepper, to taste</li><li>2 eggs</li><li>1 tablespoon sesame seeds</li><li>4 ounces (115g) lamb, cooked and sliced</li></ul>	<ul><li>Rinse the quinoa under cold water using a fine-mesh sieve. In a saucepan, combine the rinsed quinoa and water. Bring to a boil, then reduce heat to low, cover, and simmer for 15 minutes, or until the quinoa is cooked and the water is absorbed. Remove from heat and let it sit, covered, for 5 minutes. Fluff with a fork.</li><li>While the quinoa is cooking, heat the olive oil in a skillet over medium heat. Add the chopped onion and minced garlic, and sauté until softened, about 3-4 minutes.</li><li>In a large bowl, combine the cooked quinoa, sautéed onion and garlic, quartered cherry tomatoes, chopped parsley, and lemon juice. Season with salt and pepper to taste. Mix well to combine.</li><li>In a separate skillet, heat a little olive oil over medium heat. Crack the eggs into the skillet and cook until the whites are set but the yolks are still runny, about 2-3 minutes. Sprinkle the sesame seeds over the eggs while cooking.</li><li>To serve, divide the quinoa tabbouleh between serving plates. Top each serving with a sesame egg and slices of cooked lamb.</li></ul>

Wednesday

Breakfast: Eggs Florentine Breakfast Bake

Cook Time: 20 min | Prep Time: 5 min | Calories: Approximately 300 kcal	
Ingredients	**Directions**
<ul><li>1 teaspoon olive oil</li><li>1 cup (30g) fresh spinach leaves</li><li>1 large egg</li><li>1/4 cup (60ml) milk</li><li>Salt and pepper, to taste</li><li>Pinch of nutmeg</li><li>1 tablespoon grated Parmesan cheese</li></ul>	<ul><li>Preheat your oven to 375°F (190°C).</li><li>Grease a small baking dish with olive oil.</li><li>Place the fresh spinach leaves evenly at the bottom of the baking dish.</li><li>In a small bowl, whisk together the egg, milk, salt, pepper, and nutmeg.</li><li>Pour the egg mixture over the spinach leaves in the baking dish.</li><li>Sprinkle the grated Parmesan cheese over the top of the egg mixture.</li><li>Bake in the preheated oven for about 15-20 minutes, or until the eggs are set and the top is lightly golden brown.</li><li>Once cooked, remove from the oven and let it cool for a few minutes before serving.</li><li>While the breakfast bake is cooling, pour yourself a glass of milk and slice the medium apple.</li><li>Serve the Eggs Florentine Breakfast Bake with the glass of milk and sliced apple.</li></ul>

Lunch: Chicken, Cheese & Salad Wrap

Cook Time: 10 min | Prep Time: 10 min | Calories: Approximately 400 kcal	
Ingredients	**Directions**
<ul><li>1 gluten-free wrap</li><li>1 cooked chicken breast, sliced</li><li>1 slice of cheese</li><li>1/2 avocado, sliced</li><li>Assorted salad vegetables (e.g., lettuce, cucumber, carrot, capsicum)</li></ul>	<ul><li>If the chicken breast is not already cooked, cook it by grilling, baking, or pan-frying until fully cooked through. Allow it to cool slightly, then slice it into thin strips.</li><li>Lay the gluten-free wrap flat on a clean surface.</li><li>Place the slice of cheese in the center of the wrap.</li><li>Arrange the sliced chicken breast, avocado slices, and assorted salad vegetables on top of the cheese.</li><li>Carefully fold the sides of the wrap over the filling ingredients.</li><li>Starting from the bottom, tightly roll up the wrap until it forms a secure roll.</li><li>Slice the wrap in half diagonally, if desired, for easier handling.</li></ul>

Dinner: Grilled Steak with Vegetables

Cook Time: 30 min | Prep Time: 15 min | Calories: Approximately 550 kcal	
Ingredients	**Directions**
• 1 steak (about 6-8 ounces or 170-225g) • 1 tablespoon canola or olive oil • 2 medium sweet potatoes • Assorted vegetables for steaming (e.g., broccoli, carrots, green beans) • Salt and pepper, to taste	• Preheat your grill to medium-high heat. • Rub the steak with canola or olive oil and season with salt and pepper on both sides. • Place the steak on the preheated grill and cook to your desired level of doneness, about 4-5 minutes per side for medium-rare. Cooking times may vary depending on the thickness of the steak and your grill's heat. • While the steak is cooking, peel and chop the sweet potatoes into chunks. • Place the sweet potato chunks in a pot of boiling water and cook until tender, about 15-20 minutes. • While the sweet potatoes are cooking, prepare the assorted vegetables for steaming by washing and cutting them into bite-sized pieces. • Steam the vegetables until they are tender-crisp, about 5-7 minutes. • Once the steak is done cooking, remove it from the grill and let it rest for a few minutes before slicing. • Drain the cooked sweet potatoes and mash them using a potato masher or fork. Season with salt and pepper to taste. • Serve the grilled steak alongside the mashed sweet potatoes and steamed vegetables.

Thursday

Breakfast: Cereal with Milk & Fruit

Cook Time: 0 min | Prep Time: 5 min | Calories: Approximately 280 kcal	
Ingredients	**Directions**
• 2/3 cup (40g) gluten-free cereal (e.g., corn or rice flakes) • 1 cup (240ml) milk (use dairy-free milk for vegan option) • 1 medium banana, diced • 1 tablespoon (15g) linseeds (flaxseeds)	• Measure out 2/3 cup of gluten-free cereal and place it in a cereal bowl. • Dice the medium banana and add it to the bowl with the cereal. • Sprinkle the linseeds (flaxseeds) over the cereal and banana mixture. • Pour 1 cup of milk over the cereal mixture. • Stir gently to combine all the ingredients. • Let the cereal soak for a minute or two to soften slightly.

Lunch: Corn and Tuna Sweet Potatoes

Cook Time: 45 min | **Prep Time:** 5 min | **Calories:** Approximately 420 kcal	
Ingredients	**Directions**
<ul><li>1 medium sweet potato</li><li>1/4 cup (60g) canned corn kernels, drained</li><li>1/4 cup (60g) canned tuna, drained</li><li>Salt and pepper, to taste</li><li>1 tablespoon (15g) olive oil</li><li>Optional toppings: chopped parsley, grated cheese</li></ul>	<ul><li>Preheat your oven to 400°F (200°C).</li><li>Scrub the sweet potato clean and pat it dry with paper towels. Pierce the sweet potato several times with a fork.</li><li>Place the sweet potato on a baking sheet and drizzle it with olive oil. Rub the oil all over the sweet potato.</li><li>Bake the sweet potato in the preheated oven for 45-60 minutes, or until it is tender when pierced with a fork.</li><li>While the sweet potato is baking, prepare the filling. In a small bowl, mix together the canned corn kernels and canned tuna. Season with salt and pepper to taste.</li><li>Once the sweet potato is cooked, remove it from the oven and let it cool slightly.</li><li>Cut the sweet potato in half lengthwise and use a fork to gently fluff the flesh.</li><li>Spoon the corn and tuna mixture onto the sweet potato halves.</li><li>If desired, sprinkle with chopped parsley or grated cheese as toppings.</li></ul>

Dinner: Tomato Chicken Mince Buckwheat Pasta

Cook Time: 20 min | **Prep Time:** 10 min | **Calories:** Approximately 450 kcal	
Ingredients	**Directions**
<ul><li>1 cup (160g) buckwheat pasta (gluten-free)</li><li>1 cup (240ml) tomato-based sauce (gluten-free)</li><li>1/2 lb (225g) lean chicken mince</li><li>1/2 cup (75g) cherry tomatoes, halved</li><li>1 small onion, finely chopped</li><li>Roasted asparagus spears</li><li>Shredded cheese (optional)</li><li>Side salad ingredients: lettuce, cucumber, bell peppers</li><li>Vinegar dressing (gluten-free)</li><li>Salt and pepper, to taste</li></ul>	<ul><li>Cook the buckwheat pasta according to the package instructions. Drain and set aside.</li><li>In a skillet, heat a little oil over medium heat. Add the chopped onion and cook until softened, about 3-4 minutes.</li><li>Add the lean chicken mince to the skillet and cook until browned and cooked through, breaking it apart with a spatula as it cooks.</li><li>Once the chicken is cooked, add the tomato-based sauce to the skillet. Stir well to combine and let it simmer for a few minutes to heat through.</li><li>In a separate pan, roast the asparagus spears in the oven at 400°F (200°C) for about 10-12 minutes, or until tender.</li><li>Add the cooked buckwheat pasta and halved cherry tomatoes to the skillet with the chicken and sauce. Stir to combine and let it simmer for another 2-3 minutes.</li><li>Season with salt and pepper to taste.</li><li>Serve the tomato chicken mince buckwheat pasta topped with shredded cheese if desired, and alongside the roasted asparagus.</li><li>For the side salad, prepare a mix of lettuce, cucumber, and bell peppers. Drizzle with vinegar dressing.</li></ul>

Friday

Breakfast: Tomato & Avocado Toast

Cook Time: 5 min | Prep Time: 5 min | Calories: Approximately 300 kcal	
Ingredients	**Directions**
<ul><li>1 slice gluten-free bread</li><li>1 tomato, sliced</li><li>1/2 avocado, sliced</li><li>1 slice tasty cheese</li><li>1 glass (240ml) milk</li></ul>	<ul><li>Toast the gluten-free bread slice until golden brown and crispy.</li><li>While the bread is toasting, slice the tomato and avocado.</li><li>Once the bread is toasted, place it on a plate.</li><li>Layer the sliced tomato and avocado on top of the toast.</li><li>Place the slice of tasty cheese on top of the tomato and avocado.</li><li>If desired, place the assembled toast under a broiler or in a toaster oven for a minute or two until the cheese is melted and bubbly.</li><li>Serve the tomato and avocado toast immediately with a glass of milk on the side.</li></ul>

Lunch: Lentil, Vegetables & Minestrone Soup

Cook Time: 30 min | Prep Time: 10 min | Calories: Approximately 300 kcal	
Ingredients	**Directions**
<ul><li>1 cup (200g) lentils</li><li>1.5 cups (360ml) chopped vegetables (e.g., carrot, pumpkin, celery, onion)</li><li>4 cups (960ml) salt-reduced vegetable stock</li><li>1 slice gluten-free bread</li></ul>	<ul><li>Rinse the lentils under cold water using a fine-mesh sieve and drain well.</li><li>In a large pot, combine the rinsed lentils, chopped vegetables, and salt-reduced vegetable stock.</li><li>Bring the mixture to a boil over high heat, then reduce the heat to low and let it simmer for about 20-25 minutes, or until the lentils and vegetables are tender.</li><li>While the soup is simmering, toast the gluten-free bread slice until golden brown and crispy.</li><li>Once the soup is cooked and the vegetables are tender, remove the pot from the heat.</li><li>Ladle the hot soup into serving bowls.</li><li>Serve the soup immediately with the toasted gluten-free bread slice on the side.</li></ul>

Dinner: Pork Stir-Fry

Cook Time: 15 min | Prep Time: 10 min | Calories: Approximately 420 kcal	
Ingredients	**Directions**
<ul><li>100g lean pork, sliced</li><li>2 cups mixed vegetables (e.g., bell peppers, broccoli, carrots, snap peas)</li><li>1 tablespoon (15ml) canola oil</li><li>1 cup (180g) cooked brown rice</li></ul>	<ul><li>Heat the canola oil in a large skillet or wok over medium-high heat.</li><li>Add the sliced lean pork to the skillet and stir-fry until it is browned and cooked through, about 5-7 minutes. Remove the pork from the skillet and set it aside.</li><li>In the same skillet, add the mixed vegetables. Stir-fry the vegetables until they are tender-crisp, about 3-5 minutes.</li><li>Return the cooked pork to the skillet with the vegetables. Stir to combine.</li><li>Serve the pork and vegetable stir-fry hot with cooked brown rice on the side.</li></ul>

Saturday

Breakfast: Apple & Almond Pancakes

Cook Time: 10 min | Prep Time: 10 min | Calories: Approximately 350 kcal	
Ingredients	**Directions**
<ul><li>1/2 cup (40g) almond flour</li><li>1/2 teaspoon baking powder</li><li>1/4 teaspoon ground cinnamon</li><li>1/4 cup (60ml) almond milk (or any other milk of choice)</li><li>1 egg</li><li>1/2 small apple, grated</li><li>1 tablespoon (15ml) maple syrup (optional)</li><li>Cooking spray or oil for greasing the pan</li></ul>	<ul><li>In a mixing bowl, whisk together the almond flour, baking powder, and ground cinnamon.</li><li>In a separate bowl, whisk together the almond milk, egg, and maple syrup (if using) until well combined.</li><li>Pour the wet ingredients into the dry ingredients and mix until smooth.</li><li>Fold in the grated apple until evenly distributed throughout the batter.</li><li>Heat a non-stick skillet or griddle over medium heat and lightly grease it with cooking spray or oil.</li><li>Pour about 1/4 cup of the pancake batter onto the skillet for each pancake. Use the back of a spoon to spread the batter into a circle if necessary.</li><li>Cook the pancakes for 2-3 minutes on one side, or until bubbles form on the surface and the edges start to look set.</li><li>Flip the pancakes and cook for an additional 1-2 minutes on the other side, or until golden brown and cooked through.</li><li>Repeat with the remaining batter, spraying the skillet with more cooking spray or oil between batches if needed.</li><li>Serve the apple and almond pancakes warm, optionally topped with extra grated apple or a drizzle of maple syrup.</li></ul>

Lunch: Healthy Boiled Egg Salad

Cook Time: 10 min | Prep Time: 5 min | Calories: Approximately 350 kcal	
Ingredients	**Directions**
<ul><li>2 eggs</li><li>2 cups (60g) mixed salad greens</li><li>1/4 cup (15g) cherry tomatoes, halved</li><li>1/4 cup (15g) cucumber, diced</li><li>1/4 avocado, diced</li><li>1 tablespoon (15ml) olive oil</li><li>1 tablespoon (15ml) balsamic vinegar</li><li>Salt and pepper, to taste</li><li>1 slice gluten-free bread</li></ul>	<ul><li>Place the eggs in a small saucepan and cover them with water. Bring the water to a boil over high heat.</li><li>Once the water is boiling, reduce the heat to medium-low and let the eggs simmer for 8-10 minutes for hard-boiled eggs.</li><li>While the eggs are boiling, prepare a bowl of ice water. Once the eggs are done cooking, immediately transfer them to the ice water bath to stop the cooking process.</li><li>While the eggs are cooling, prepare the salad. In a large bowl, combine the mixed salad greens, halved cherry tomatoes, diced cucumber, and diced avocado.</li><li>In a small bowl, whisk together the olive oil and balsamic vinegar to make the dressing. Season with salt and pepper to taste.</li><li>Once the eggs are cooled, peel them and slice them into halves or quarters.</li><li>Add the sliced boiled eggs to the salad bowl.</li><li>Drizzle the salad with the prepared dressing and toss gently to coat.</li><li>Toast the gluten-free bread slice until golden brown and crispy.</li><li>Serve the healthy boiled egg salad with the toasted gluten-free bread slice on the side.</li></ul>

Dinner: Beef & Black Bean Stir-fry with Rice Noodles

Cook Time: 10 min | Prep Time: 15 min | Calories: Approximately 400 kcal	
Ingredients	**Directions**
<ul><li>130g lean beef, thinly sliced</li><li>1.5 cups (225g) cooked mixed vegetables (e.g., carrot, mushroom, celery, capsicum, snow peas)</li><li>1/4 cup (60g) black beans</li><li>1 cup (140g) cooked rice noodles</li><li>2 teaspoons (10ml) sesame oil for cooking</li></ul>	<ul><li>Cook the rice noodles according to the package instructions. Drain and set aside.</li><li>Heat 1 teaspoon of sesame oil in a large skillet or wok over medium-high heat.</li><li>Add the thinly sliced lean beef to the skillet and stir-fry until browned and cooked through, about 2-3 minutes. Remove the beef from the skillet and set aside.</li><li>In the same skillet, add the remaining teaspoon of sesame oil.</li><li>Add the cooked mixed vegetables to the skillet and stir-fry for 3-4 minutes, or until they are tender-crisp.</li><li>Return the cooked beef to the skillet with the vegetables.</li><li>Add the black beans to the skillet and stir to combine.</li><li>Add the cooked rice noodles to the skillet and toss everything together until well mixed and heated through.</li><li>Cook for an additional 1-2 minutes, stirring frequently.</li><li>Once everything is heated through, remove the skillet from the heat.</li><li>Serve the beef and black bean stir-fry with rice noodles immediately.</li></ul>

Sunday

Breakfast: Muesli with Yogurt & Fruit

Cook Time: 0 min | Prep Time: 5 min | Calories: Approximately 300 kcal	
Ingredients	**Directions**
<ul><li>1/2 cup (40g) gluten-free muesli</li><li>1 tub (150g) yogurt (choose a gluten-free variety)</li><li>2 nectarines, apricots, or plums, diced</li></ul>	<ul><li>Place the gluten-free muesli in a bowl.</li><li>Add the yogurt on top of the muesli.</li><li>Dice the nectarines, apricots, or plums, and add them to the bowl.</li><li>Stir all the ingredients together until well combined.</li></ul>

Lunch: Mushroom and Tomato Omelette

Cook Time: 10 min | Prep Time: 5 min | Calories: Approximately 250 kcal	
Ingredients	**Directions**
<ul><li>2 large eggs</li><li>1/4 cup (30g) sliced mushrooms</li><li>1/4 cup (60g) diced tomatoes</li><li>Salt and pepper, to taste</li><li>1 tablespoon (15ml) olive oil</li><li>1 slice gluten-free bread</li></ul>	<ul><li>Heat the olive oil in a non-stick skillet over medium heat.</li><li>While the skillet is heating, crack the eggs into a bowl and beat them until well combined. Season with salt and pepper to taste.</li><li>Add the sliced mushrooms to the skillet and cook for 2-3 minutes, until they start to soften.</li><li>Add the diced tomatoes to the skillet and cook for another 1-2 minutes, until they begin to release their juices.</li><li>Pour the beaten eggs into the skillet, making sure they cover the mushrooms and tomatoes evenly.</li><li>Cook the omelette for 2-3 minutes, or until the edges start to set.</li><li>Using a spatula, gently lift the edges of the omelette and tilt the skillet to let any uncooked egg run underneath.</li><li>Once the omelette is mostly set but still slightly runny on top, fold it in half using the spatula.</li><li>Cook for another 1-2 minutes, or until the omelette is cooked through and no longer runny.</li><li>While the omelette is cooking, toast the gluten-free bread until golden brown.</li><li>Serve the mushroom and tomato omelette hot, with the toasted gluten-free bread on the side.</li></ul>

Dinner: Baked Salmon with Quinoa & Vegetables

Cook Time: 20 min	**Prep Time:** 10 min	**Calories:** Approximately 400 kcal	

Ingredients	Directions
<ul><li>1 medium salmon fillet (100g)</li><li>1 cup (185g) cooked quinoa</li><li>2 cups (300g) cooked vegetables (e.g., cauliflower, broccoli, carrots)</li><li>2 teaspoons (10ml) oil (for cooking or dressing)</li><li>Lemon juice, to taste</li><li>Salt and pepper, to taste</li></ul>	<ul><li>Preheat your oven to 375°F (190°C).</li><li>Season the salmon fillet with salt and pepper to taste.</li><li>Place the seasoned salmon fillet on a baking sheet lined with parchment paper.</li><li>Bake the salmon in the preheated oven for 15-20 minutes, or until it is cooked through and flakes easily with a fork.</li><li>While the salmon is baking, prepare the quinoa and vegetables.</li><li>Cook the quinoa according to the package instructions. Once cooked, fluff it with a fork and set it aside.</li><li>Steam or boil the vegetables until they are tender-crisp. Drain any excess water and set aside.</li><li>In a small bowl, whisk together the oil and lemon juice to make a dressing.</li><li>Once the salmon is done baking, remove it from the oven and let it rest for a few minutes.</li><li>To serve, divide the cooked quinoa and vegetables among serving plates.</li><li>Place a portion of the baked salmon on top of each plate.</li><li>Drizzle the oil and lemon juice dressing over the quinoa, vegetables, and salmon.</li></ul>

Chapter 5: Gluten-Free Recipes

Breakfast Recipes

Muesli with Almond Milk

 Breakfast

 Cook time: 0 min

 Prep time: 5 min

 Servings: 2

Ingredients:

- 1 cup (90 g) gluten-free rolled oats
- 1/4 cup (40 g) dried fruits (such as raisins, cranberries, chopped apricots)
- 2 tablespoons (30 g) nuts (such as almonds, walnuts, pecans), chopped
- 2 tablespoons (30 g) seeds (such as pumpkin seeds, sunflower seeds, chia seeds)
- 1 tablespoon (15 g) honey or maple syrup (optional)
- 1 cup (240 ml) almond milk (or any preferred milk)

Directions:

- In a mixing bowl, combine the gluten-free rolled oats, dried fruits, chopped nuts, and seeds.

- If desired, drizzle honey or maple syrup over the mixture for added sweetness. Stir well to combine.

- Divide the muesli mixture between two serving bowls.

- Pour almond milk over the muesli mixture in each bowl, covering it completely.

- Let the muesli sit for a few minutes to allow the oats to soak up the almond milk and soften slightly.

- Optionally, you can refrigerate the muesli overnight for a softer texture and to allow the flavors to meld.

- Serve the muesli with almond milk as is, or top with additional fresh fruits or a dollop of yogurt if desired.

Nutritional Value (Per Serving):

- Calories: Approximately 320 kcal
- Fat: 12g
- Cholesterol: 0mg
- Sodium: 80mg
- Carbohydrates: 47g
- Protein: 8g

Banana Pancakes

Breakfast

Cook time:
10 min

Prep time:
10 min

Servings:
2

Ingredients:

- 2 ripe bananas
- 2 large eggs
- 1/2 teaspoon (2.5 ml) vanilla extract
- 1/2 teaspoon (2.5 ml) ground cinnamon
- 1/4 teaspoon (1.25 ml) baking powder
- Pinch of salt
- Butter or oil, for cooking
- **Optional toppings:** maple syrup, sliced bananas, berries, nuts

Directions:

- In a medium mixing bowl, mash the ripe bananas until smooth.

- Add the eggs, vanilla extract, ground cinnamon, baking powder, and a pinch of salt to the mashed bananas. Mix until well combined.

- Heat a non-stick skillet or griddle over medium heat and add a small amount of butter or oil to coat the surface.

- Once the skillet is hot, pour about 1/4 cup (60 ml) of the pancake batter onto the skillet for each pancake. You may need to spread the batter slightly with the back of a spoon to form circles.

- Cook the pancakes for 2-3 minutes on one side, or until bubbles start to form on the surface.

- Flip the pancakes and cook for an additional 1-2 minutes on the other side, or until golden brown and cooked through.

- Repeat with the remaining batter, adding more butter or oil to the skillet as needed.

- Once all the pancakes are cooked, serve them warm with your favorite toppings such as maple syrup, sliced bananas, berries, or nuts.

Nutritional Value (Per Serving):

- Calories: Approximately 240 kcal
- Fat: 8g
- Cholesterol: 186mg
- Sodium: 184mg
- Carbohydrates: 38g
- Protein: 8g

Greek Yogurt Parfait with Granola

Breakfast

Cook time:
0 min

Prep time:
5 min

Servings:
2

Ingredients:

- 1 cup (240 g) Greek yogurt
- 1/2 cup (120 ml) granola (ensure it's gluten-free)
- 1/2 cup (75 g) mixed berries (such as strawberries, blueberries, raspberries)
- 2 tablespoons (30 ml) honey or maple syrup
- **Optional:** sliced bananas, chopped nuts, shredded coconut for topping

Directions:

- In two serving glasses or bowls, spoon a layer of Greek yogurt into the bottom of each.

- Add a layer of granola on top of the yogurt in each glass.

- Top the granola layer with mixed berries, distributing them evenly between the glasses.

- Drizzle honey or maple syrup over the berries.

- Repeat the layers - yogurt, granola, berries, and honey - until the glasses are filled, ending with a final drizzle of honey or maple syrup.

- If desired, add optional toppings such as sliced bananas, chopped nuts, or shredded coconut on top.

Nutritional Value (Per Serving):

- Calories: Approximately 300 kcal
- Fat: 10g
- Cholesterol: 10mg
- Sodium: 50mg
- Carbohydrates: 45g
- Protein: 15g

Scrambled Eggs with Avocado Toast

Breakfast

Cook time:
10 min

Prep time:
5 min

Servings:
2

Ingredients:

- 4 large eggs
- 1 ripe avocado
- 2 slices gluten-free bread
- 2 tablespoons (30 ml) milk
- Salt and pepper to taste
- 1 tablespoon (15 ml) olive oil
- **Optional toppings:** chopped herbs, hot sauce

Directions:

- In a small mixing bowl, crack the eggs and add the milk, salt, and pepper. Beat the mixture until well combined.

- Heat olive oil in a non-stick skillet over medium heat.

- Once the skillet is hot, pour the egg mixture into the skillet.

- Using a spatula, continuously stir the eggs gently until they are cooked to your desired consistency, about 3-4 minutes. Remove from heat.

- While the eggs are cooking, toast the gluten-free bread slices until golden brown.

- Cut the avocado in half, remove the pit, and scoop the flesh into a small bowl. Mash the avocado with a fork until smooth.

- Spread the mashed avocado evenly onto the toasted bread slices.

- Divide the scrambled eggs between the avocado toast slices.

- Optional: Garnish with chopped herbs and hot sauce, if desired.

Nutritional Value (Per Serving):

- Calories: Approximately 380 kcal
- Fat: 25g
- Cholesterol: 372mg
- Sodium: 310mg
- Carbohydrates: 22g
- Protein: 20g

Chia Seed Pudding with Mango

Breakfast

Cook time:
0 min (2hr+ chilling time)

Prep time:
5 min

Servings:
2

Ingredients:

- 1/4 cup (48 g) chia seeds
- 1 cup (240 ml) coconut milk (or any preferred milk)
- 1 tablespoon (15 ml) honey or maple syrup
- 1/2 teaspoon (2.5 ml) vanilla extract
- 1 ripe mango, peeled and diced

Directions:

- In a mixing bowl, combine the chia seeds, coconut milk, honey or maple syrup, and vanilla extract. Stir well to ensure the chia seeds are evenly distributed.

- Let the mixture sit for 5 minutes, then stir again to break up any clumps of chia seeds.

- Cover the bowl and refrigerate for at least 2 hours or overnight, allowing the chia seeds to absorb the liquid and thicken.

- Once the chia pudding has thickened to your desired consistency, remove it from the refrigerator.

- Divide the chia pudding between serving glasses or bowls.

- Top each serving with diced mango.

Nutritional Value (Per Serving):

- Calories: Approximately 290 kcal
- Fat: 17g
- Cholesterol: 0mg
- Sodium: 20mg
- Carbohydrates: 31g
- Protein: 6g

Smoothie Bowl with Mixed Fruits and Nuts

Breakfast

Cook time:
0 min

Prep time:
5 min

Servings:
2

Ingredients:

- 2 ripe bananas, sliced and frozen
- 1 cup (150 g) mixed berries (such as strawberries, blueberries, raspberries)
- 1/2 cup (120 ml) unsweetened almond milk (or any preferred milk)
- 2 tablespoons (30 g) Greek yogurt
- 2 tablespoons (30 g) mixed nuts (such as almonds, walnuts, cashews), chopped
- 2 tablespoons (30 g) shredded coconut
- **Optional toppings:** additional mixed fruits, seeds (such as chia seeds, hemp seeds), honey or maple syrup

Directions:

- In a blender, combine the frozen banana slices, mixed berries, almond milk, and Greek yogurt.

- Blend until smooth and creamy, adding more almond milk if needed to reach your desired consistency.

- Pour the smoothie mixture into two serving bowls.

- Top each bowl with chopped mixed nuts and shredded coconut.

- Add additional mixed fruits and seeds on top if desired.

- Optional: Drizzle honey or maple syrup over the smoothie bowls for added sweetness.

Nutritional Value (Per Serving):

- Calories: Approximately 280 kcal
- Fat: 12g
- Cholesterol: 2mg
- Sodium: 80mg
- Carbohydrates: 40g
- Protein: 7g

Omelette with Spinach and Feta

Breakfast

Cook time:
10 min

Prep time:
5 min

Servings:
2

Ingredients:

- 4 large eggs
- 1 cup (240 ml) fresh spinach, chopped
- 1/4 cup (60 g) feta cheese, crumbled
- 2 tablespoons (30 ml) milk
- Salt and pepper to taste
- 1 tablespoon (15 ml) olive oil

Directions:

- In a medium-sized mixing bowl, crack the eggs and beat them lightly with a fork or whisk.

- Add the chopped spinach, crumbled feta cheese, milk, salt, and pepper to the eggs. Mix well until all ingredients are combined.

- Heat olive oil in a non-stick skillet over medium heat.

- Once the skillet is hot, pour the egg mixture into the skillet, spreading it evenly.

- Allow the omelette to cook undisturbed for about 2-3 minutes until the edges start to set.

- Using a spatula, gently lift the edges of the omelette and tilt the skillet to let the uncooked egg mixture flow underneath.

- Continue cooking for another 2-3 minutes or until the omelette is mostly set but still slightly runny on top.

- Carefully fold one side of the omelette over the other using a spatula, creating a half-moon shape. Cook for an additional 1-2 minutes to ensure the inside is fully cooked.

- Once cooked to your desired consistency, transfer the omelette to a plate and serve hot.

Nutritional Value (Per Serving):

- Calories: Approximately 232 kcal
- Fat: 17g
- Cholesterol: 373mg
- Sodium: 388mg
- Carbohydrates: 2g
- Protein: 17g

Sweet Potato Hash Browns with Eggs

Breakfast

Cook time:
20 min

Prep time:
10 min

Servings:
2

Ingredients:

- 1 large sweet potato (about 300 g), peeled and grated
- 2 tablespoons (30 ml) olive oil
- 1/2 teaspoon (2.5 g) salt
- 1/4 teaspoon (1.25 g) black pepper
- 1/2 teaspoon (2.5 g) garlic powder
- 2 large eggs
- **Optional toppings:** sliced avocado, chopped parsley, hot sauce

Directions:

- Place the grated sweet potato in a clean kitchen towel and squeeze out any excess moisture.

- In a mixing bowl, combine the grated sweet potato with salt, pepper, and garlic powder. Mix well to coat the sweet potato evenly.

- Heat olive oil in a non-stick skillet over medium heat.

- Once the skillet is hot, add the sweet potato mixture, spreading it out evenly to form a layer.

- Cook the sweet potato hash browns for about 4-5 minutes on each side, or until crispy and golden brown. Use a spatula to flip them halfway through cooking.

- While the hash browns are cooking, prepare the eggs. In another skillet, heat a little olive oil over medium heat. Crack the eggs into the skillet and cook until the whites are set but the yolks are still runny, about 3-4 minutes.

- Once the hash browns are crispy and the eggs are cooked to your liking, transfer them to serving plates.

- Top each serving of sweet potato hash browns with a fried egg.

- Garnish with optional toppings such as sliced avocado, chopped parsley, or hot sauce, if desired.

Nutritional Value (Per Serving):

- Calories: Approximately 320 kcal
- Fat: 20g
- Cholesterol: 190mg
- Sodium: 640mg
- Carbohydrates: 27g
- Protein: 11g

Coconut Flour Waffles with Maple Syrup

Breakfast

Cook time:
10 min

Prep time:
10 min

Servings:
4

Ingredients:

- 1/2 cup (56g) coconut flour
- 1 teaspoon (5g) baking powder
- 1/4 teaspoon (1.25g) salt
- 4 large eggs
- 1/2 cup (120ml) almond milk (or any preferred milk)
- 2 tablespoons (30ml) maple syrup, plus extra for serving
- 2 tablespoons (28g) coconut oil, melted
- 1 teaspoon (5ml) vanilla extract

Directions:

- Preheat your waffle iron according to manufacturer's instructions.

- In a large mixing bowl, whisk together the coconut flour, baking powder, and salt until well combined.

- In another bowl, beat the eggs. Then add almond milk, maple syrup, melted coconut oil, and vanilla extract. Mix until smooth.

- Pour the wet ingredients into the dry ingredients and whisk until there are no lumps and the batter is smooth.

- Lightly grease the waffle iron with coconut oil or non-stick spray.

- Pour the batter onto the preheated waffle iron, spreading it evenly.

- Close the waffle iron and cook according to manufacturer's instructions, usually about 3-5 minutes, or until the waffles are golden brown and crispy.

- Carefully remove the waffles from the iron and place them on a plate.

- Serve the coconut flour waffles warm with maple syrup drizzled on top.

Nutritional Value (Per Serving):

- Calories: Approximately 230 kcal
- Fat: 14g
- Cholesterol: 186mg
- Sodium: 330mg
- Carbohydrates: 18g
- Protein: 7g

Buckwheat Pancakes with Blueberry Compote

Breakfast

Cook time:
15 min

Prep time:
10 min

Servings:
4

Ingredients:

For Buckwheat Pancakes:
- 1 cup (120g) buckwheat flour
- 1 tablespoon (12g) sugar
- 1 teaspoon (5g) baking powder
- 1/2 teaspoon (3g) baking soda
- Pinch of salt
- 1 cup (240ml) almond milk (or any preferred milk)
- 1 large egg
- 2 tablespoons (30ml) melted coconut oil (or butter)
- 1 teaspoon (5ml) vanilla extract

For Blueberry Compote:
- 1 cup (150g) fresh or frozen blueberries
- 2 tablespoons (30ml) water
- 1 tablespoon (12g) sugar
- 1/2 tablespoon (7ml) lemon juice
- **Optional toppings:** Greek yogurt, additional fresh blueberries, maple syrup

Nutritional Value (Per Serving):

- Calories: Approximately 290 kcal
- Fat: 10g
- Cholesterol: 47mg
- Sodium: 310mg
- Carbohydrates: 45g
- Protein: 7g

Directions:

- In a large mixing bowl, whisk together the buckwheat flour, sugar, baking powder, baking soda, and salt.

- In another bowl, whisk together the almond milk, egg, melted coconut oil, and vanilla extract until well combined.

- Pour the wet ingredients into the dry ingredients and stir until just combined. Be careful not to overmix; a few lumps are okay.

- Heat a non-stick skillet or griddle over medium heat and lightly grease with coconut oil or butter.

- Pour about 1/4 cup of batter onto the skillet for each pancake. Cook until bubbles form on the surface, then flip and cook until golden brown on the other side. Repeat with the remaining batter.

- While the pancakes are cooking, prepare the blueberry compote. In a small saucepan, combine the blueberries, water, sugar, and lemon juice. Cook over medium heat, stirring occasionally, until the blueberries soften and release their juices, about 5 minutes. Use a fork to lightly mash some of the blueberries for a chunky compote.

- Serve the buckwheat pancakes warm with a spoonful of blueberry compote on top. Optionally, top with Greek yogurt, additional fresh blueberries, and a drizzle of maple syrup.

Shakshuka

Breakfast	Cook time: 25 min	Prep time: 10 min	Servings: 4

Ingredients:

- 2 tablespoons (30 ml) olive oil
- 1 onion, diced
- 1 red bell pepper, diced
- 3 cloves garlic, minced
- 1 teaspoon (5 g) ground cumin
- 1 teaspoon (5 g) paprika
- 1/2 teaspoon (2.5 g) ground coriander
- 1/4 teaspoon (1.25 g) cayenne pepper (optional, for heat)
- 1 can (14 oz/400 g) diced tomatoes
- 1 can (14 oz/400 g) crushed tomatoes
- Salt and pepper, to taste
- 4-6 large eggs
- Fresh parsley or cilantro, chopped (for garnish)
- Feta cheese or crumbled goat cheese (optional, for serving)
- Gluten-free bread or pita (optional, for serving)

Nutritional Value (Per Serving):

- Calories: Approximately 220 kcal
- Fat: 15g
- Cholesterol: 210mg
- Sodium: 480mg
- Carbohydrates: 15g
- Protein: 10g

Directions:

- Heat olive oil in a large skillet or cast-iron pan over medium heat.

- Add diced onion and bell pepper to the skillet and sauté until softened, about 5 minutes.

- Add minced garlic, ground cumin, paprika, ground coriander, and cayenne pepper (if using) to the skillet. Cook for another 1-2 minutes until fragrant.

- Pour in the diced tomatoes and crushed tomatoes. Season with salt and pepper to taste. Stir well to combine.

- Simmer the tomato sauce over medium-low heat for about 10-15 minutes, until it thickens slightly.

- Using a spoon, create small wells in the tomato sauce. Crack one egg into each well.

- Cover the skillet and continue to cook for about 5-7 minutes, or until the egg whites are set but the yolks are still runny, or longer if you prefer firmer yolks.

- Once the eggs are cooked to your liking, remove the skillet from the heat.

- Garnish with chopped parsley or cilantro and crumbled feta cheese or goat cheese, if desired.

- Serve the shakshuka hot, directly from the skillet, with gluten-free bread or pita for dipping if desired.

Overnight Oats with Almond Milk and Chia Seeds

Breakfast

Cook time:
0 min (4hr+ chilling time)

Prep time:
5 min

Servings:
2

Ingredients:

- 1 cup (90g) rolled oats
- 1 cup (240ml) almond milk (or any preferred milk)
- 2 tablespoons (30g) chia seeds
- 1 tablespoon (15ml) maple syrup or honey
- 1/2 teaspoon (2.5ml) vanilla extract
- Pinch of salt
- **Optional toppings:** fresh berries, sliced bananas, nuts, seeds, coconut flakes

Directions:

- In a mixing bowl or jar, combine the rolled oats, almond milk, chia seeds, maple syrup or honey, vanilla extract, and a pinch of salt. Stir well to combine.

- Cover the bowl or jar and refrigerate overnight, or for at least 4 hours, to allow the oats and chia seeds to absorb the liquid and soften.

- The next morning, give the overnight oats a good stir. If the mixture is too thick, you can add a splash of almond milk to reach your desired consistency.

- Divide the overnight oats into serving bowls.

- Top each serving with your favorite toppings such as fresh berries, sliced bananas, nuts, seeds, or coconut flakes.

- Serve cold and enjoy your delicious and nutritious gluten-free overnight oats with almond milk and chia seeds!

Nutritional Value (Per Serving):

- Calories: Approximately 290 kcal
- Fat: 9g
- Cholesterol: 0mg
- Sodium: 70mg
- Carbohydrates: 46g
- Protein: 9g

Soup Recipes

Butternut Squash Soup

Soup

Cook time:
40 min

Prep time:
15 min

Servings:
4

Ingredients:

- 1 medium-sized butternut squash (about 2 pounds/900g), peeled, seeded, and cubed
- 1 tablespoon (15ml) olive oil
- 1 onion, chopped
- 2 cloves garlic, minced
- 1 teaspoon (5g) ground cumin
- 1/2 teaspoon (2.5g) ground cinnamon
- 1/4 teaspoon (1.25g) ground nutmeg
- 4 cups (960ml) vegetable broth
- Salt and pepper, to taste
- **Optional toppings:** Greek yogurt, pumpkin seeds, chopped fresh herbs

Nutritional Value (Per Serving):

- Calories: Approximately 180 kcal
- Fat: 4g
- Cholesterol: 0mg
- Sodium: 800mg
- Carbohydrates: 38g
- Protein: 4g

Directions:

- In a large pot, heat the olive oil over medium heat. Add the chopped onion and sauté until translucent, about 5 minutes.

- Add the minced garlic to the pot and cook for another 1-2 minutes, until fragrant.

- Stir in the cubed butternut squash, ground cumin, ground cinnamon, and ground nutmeg. Cook for 5 minutes, stirring occasionally.

- Pour the vegetable broth into the pot, covering the butternut squash mixture. Bring to a boil, then reduce the heat to low. Simmer, covered, for about 25-30 minutes, or until the butternut squash is tender and easily pierced with a fork.

- Once the butternut squash is cooked through, remove the pot from the heat. Use an immersion blender to purée the soup until smooth. Alternatively, you can transfer the soup in batches to a blender and blend until smooth. Be cautious with hot liquids in a blender; work in batches and vent the lid.

- Season the soup with salt and pepper to taste. Adjust the seasonings if necessary.

- Serve the butternut squash soup hot, garnished with a dollop of Greek yogurt, pumpkin seeds, and chopped fresh herbs if desired.

Lentil Soup with Vegetables

Soup

Cook time:
45 min

Prep time:
15 min

Servings:
6

Ingredients:

- 1 cup (200g) dried lentils, rinsed and drained
- 1 tablespoon (15ml) olive oil
- 1 onion, chopped
- 2 carrots, peeled and diced
- 2 celery stalks, diced
- 2 cloves garlic, minced
- 1 teaspoon (5g) ground cumin
- 1 teaspoon (5g) ground coriander
- 1/2 teaspoon (2.5g) smoked paprika
- 6 cups (1440ml) vegetable broth
- 1 can (14 oz/400g) diced tomatoes, undrained
- 2 cups (300g) chopped spinach or kale
- Salt and pepper, to taste
- Fresh parsley or cilantro, chopped (for garnish)

Directions:

- Heat the olive oil in a large pot over medium heat. Add the chopped onion, carrots, and celery. Sauté until the vegetables are softened, about 5 minutes.

- Add the minced garlic, ground cumin, ground coriander, and smoked paprika to the pot. Cook for another 1-2 minutes, until fragrant.

- Pour in the vegetable broth and diced tomatoes (with their juices). Stir well to combine.

- Add the rinsed and drained lentils to the pot. Bring the soup to a boil, then reduce the heat to low. Cover and simmer for 30-35 minutes, or until the lentils are tender.

- Stir in the chopped spinach or kale, and continue to simmer for an additional 5 minutes, until the greens are wilted.

- Season the soup with salt and pepper to taste. Adjust the seasonings if necessary.

- Serve the lentil soup hot, garnished with chopped fresh parsley or cilantro.

Nutritional Value (Per Serving):

- Calories: Approximately 220 kcal
- Fat: 4g
- Cholesterol: 0mg
- Sodium: 800mg
- Carbohydrates: 35g
- Protein: 13g

Chicken and Rice Soup

Soup

Cook time:
45 min

Prep time:
10 min

Servings:
6

Ingredients:

- 1 tablespoon (15ml) olive oil
- 1 onion, diced
- 2 carrots, diced
- 2 celery stalks, diced
- 2 cloves garlic, minced
- 1 teaspoon (5g) dried thyme
- 1 teaspoon (5g) dried oregano
- 6 cups (1440ml) chicken broth (ensure it's gluten-free)
- 1 cup (185g) long-grain white rice
- 2 cups (300g) cooked chicken breast, shredded or diced
- Salt and pepper, to taste
- Fresh parsley, chopped (for garnish)

Directions:

- In a large pot, heat the olive oil over medium heat. Add the diced onion, carrots, and celery. Sauté until the vegetables are softened, about 5 minutes.

- Add the minced garlic, dried thyme, and dried oregano to the pot. Cook for another 1-2 minutes, until fragrant.

- Pour in the chicken broth and bring to a boil.

- Add the long-grain white rice to the pot. Reduce the heat to low, cover, and simmer for 15-20 minutes, or until the rice is cooked through and tender.

- Once the rice is cooked, stir in the cooked chicken breast. Simmer for an additional 5 minutes to heat the chicken through.

- Season the soup with salt and pepper to taste. Adjust the seasonings if necessary.

- Ladle the chicken and rice soup into bowls. Garnish with chopped fresh parsley.

Nutritional Value (Per Serving):

- Calories: Approximately 280 kcal
- Fat: 6g
- Cholesterol: 40mg
- Sodium: 800mg
- Carbohydrates: 32g
- Protein: 24g

Tomato Basil Soup

Soup

Cook time:
45 min

Prep time:
10 min

Servings:
4

Ingredients:

- 2 tablespoons (30ml) olive oil
- 1 onion, chopped
- 2 cloves garlic, minced
- 2 cans (14 oz/400g each) diced tomatoes
- 1 can (14 oz/400g) tomato sauce
- 2 cups (480ml) vegetable broth (ensure it's gluten-free)
- 1/4 cup (10g) fresh basil leaves, chopped
- 1 teaspoon (5g) dried oregano
- Salt and pepper, to taste
- **Optional toppings:** fresh basil leaves, drizzle of olive oil, dollop of Greek yogurt or cream

Directions:

- Heat the olive oil in a large pot over medium heat. Add the chopped onion and cook until translucent, about 5 minutes.

- Add the minced garlic to the pot and cook for another 1-2 minutes, until fragrant.

- Pour in the diced tomatoes (with their juices), tomato sauce, and vegetable broth. Stir to combine.

- Add the chopped basil leaves and dried oregano to the pot. Season with salt and pepper to taste.

- Bring the soup to a boil, then reduce the heat to low. Cover and simmer for 30 minutes, stirring occasionally.

- Once the soup has simmered and the flavors have melded together, remove the pot from the heat.

- Use an immersion blender to blend the soup until smooth. Alternatively, carefully transfer the soup to a blender and blend in batches until smooth. Be cautious with hot liquids in a blender; work in batches and vent the lid.

- Taste and adjust the seasonings if necessary.

- Serve the tomato basil soup hot, garnished with additional fresh basil leaves, a drizzle of olive oil, and a dollop of Greek yogurt or cream if desired.

Nutritional Value (Per Serving):

- Calories: Approximately 150 kcal
- Fat: 7g
- Cholesterol: 0mg
- Sodium: 800mg
- Carbohydrates: 20g
- Protein: 3g

Potato Leek Soup

Soup

Cook time:
30 min

Prep time:
15 min

Servings:
4

Ingredients:

- 2 tablespoons (30ml) olive oil
- 2 leeks, white and light green parts only, thinly sliced
- 2 cloves garlic, minced
- 4 medium potatoes (about 600g), peeled and diced
- 4 cups (960ml) vegetable broth (ensure it's gluten-free)
- 1 bay leaf
- Salt and pepper, to taste
- **Optional toppings:** chopped fresh chives, crispy bacon bits, drizzle of olive oil, dollop of Greek yogurt or cream

Directions:

- In a large pot, heat the olive oil over medium heat. Add the sliced leeks and cook until softened, about 5 minutes.

- Add the minced garlic to the pot and cook for another 1-2 minutes, until fragrant.

- Add the diced potatoes, vegetable broth, and bay leaf to the pot. Stir to combine.

- Bring the soup to a boil, then reduce the heat to low. Cover and simmer for 15-20 minutes, or until the potatoes are tender.

- Once the potatoes are cooked through, remove the bay leaf from the pot.

- Use an immersion blender to blend the soup until smooth. Alternatively, carefully transfer the soup to a blender and blend in batches until smooth. Be cautious with hot liquids in a blender; work in batches and vent the lid.

- Season the soup with salt and pepper to taste. Adjust the seasonings if necessary.

- Serve the potato leek soup hot, garnished with chopped fresh chives, crispy bacon bits, a drizzle of olive oil, or a dollop of Greek yogurt or cream if desired.

Nutritional Value (Per Serving):

- Calories: Approximately 200 kcal
- Fat: 7g
- Cholesterol: 0mg
- Sodium: 700mg
- Carbohydrates: 30g
- Protein: 4g

Carrot Ginger Soup

Soup

Cook time:
30 min

Prep time:
10 min

Servings:
4

Ingredients:

- 1 tablespoon (15ml) olive oil
- 1 onion, chopped
- 1 lb (450g) carrots, peeled and sliced
- 2 cloves garlic, minced
- 1 tablespoon (15g) fresh ginger, grated
- 4 cups (960ml) vegetable broth (ensure it's gluten-free)
- Salt and pepper, to taste
- **Optional toppings:** chopped fresh cilantro or parsley, Greek yogurt or coconut cream, toasted pumpkin seeds

Directions:

- In a large pot, heat the olive oil over medium heat. Add the chopped onion and sauté until softened, about 5 minutes.

- Add the sliced carrots, minced garlic, and grated ginger to the pot. Sauté for another 2-3 minutes, until fragrant.

- Pour in the vegetable broth, ensuring that the carrots are fully submerged. Bring to a boil, then reduce the heat to low. Cover and simmer for 20-25 minutes, or until the carrots are tender.

- Once the carrots are cooked through, remove the pot from the heat.

- Use an immersion blender to blend the soup until smooth. Alternatively, carefully transfer the soup to a blender and blend in batches until smooth. Be cautious with hot liquids in a blender; work in batches and vent the lid.

- Season the soup with salt and pepper to taste. Adjust the seasonings if necessary.

- Serve the carrot ginger soup hot, garnished with chopped fresh cilantro or parsley, a dollop of Greek yogurt or coconut cream, and toasted pumpkin seeds if desired.

Nutritional Value (Per Serving):

- Calories: Approximately 120 kcal
- Fat: 3g
- Cholesterol: 0mg
- Sodium: 800mg
- Carbohydrates: 22g
- Protein: 2g

Mexican Chicken Soup

| Soup | Cook time: 30 min | Prep time: 15 min | Servings: 4 |

Ingredients:

- 1 tablespoon (15ml) olive oil
- 1 onion, chopped
- 2 cloves garlic, minced
- 1 jalapeño pepper, seeded and diced
- 1 teaspoon (5g) ground cumin
- 1 teaspoon (5g) chili powder
- 1/2 teaspoon (2.5g) smoked paprika
- 4 cups (960ml) chicken broth (ensure it's gluten-free)
- 1 can (14 oz/400g) diced tomatoes, undrained
- 1 cup (150g) corn kernels (fresh, frozen, or canned)
- 1 cup (150g) black beans, drained and rinsed
- 2 cups (300g) cooked shredded chicken
- Juice of 1 lime
- Salt and pepper, to taste
- **Optional toppings:** chopped fresh cilantro, diced avocado, lime wedges, sliced jalapeños, Greek yogurt or sour cream

Directions:

- In a large pot, heat the olive oil over medium heat. Add the chopped onion and cook until softened, about 5 minutes.

- Add the minced garlic and diced jalapeño pepper to the pot. Cook for another 1-2 minutes, until fragrant.

- Stir in the ground cumin, chili powder, and smoked paprika. Cook for another minute to toast the spices.

- Pour in the chicken broth and diced tomatoes with their juices. Bring the soup to a simmer.

- Add the corn kernels, black beans, and cooked shredded chicken to the pot. Simmer for 10-15 minutes to allow the flavors to meld together.

- Squeeze in the juice of one lime and season the soup with salt and pepper to taste. Adjust the seasonings if necessary.

- Serve the Mexican chicken soup hot, garnished with chopped fresh cilantro, diced avocado, lime wedges, sliced jalapeños, and a dollop of Greek yogurt or sour cream if desired.

Nutritional Value (Per Serving):

- Calories: Approximately 280 kcal
- Fat: 7g
- Cholesterol: 40mg
- Sodium: 800mg
- Carbohydrates: 30g
- Protein: 25g

Thai Coconut Curry Soup with Shrimp

Soup

Cook time:
25 min

Prep time:
15 min

Servings:
4

Ingredients:

- 1 tablespoon (15ml) vegetable oil
- 1 onion, finely chopped
- 2 cloves garlic, minced
- 1 red bell pepper, thinly sliced
- 2 tablespoons (30g) Thai red curry paste
- 1 can (14 oz/400ml) coconut milk
- 3 cups (720ml) chicken or vegetable broth (ensure it's gluten-free)
- 1 tablespoon (15ml) fish sauce
- 1 tablespoon (15ml) lime juice
- 1 tablespoon (15ml) brown sugar
- 1 cup (150g) sliced mushrooms
- 1 lb (450g) shrimp, peeled and deveined
- 2 cups (60g) baby spinach leaves
- Salt and pepper, to taste
- Fresh cilantro, chopped (for garnish)
- Cooked rice or rice noodles, for serving

Nutritional Value (Per Serving):

- Calories: Approximately 350 kcal
- Fat: 22g
- Cholesterol: 200mg
- Sodium: 1000mg
- Carbohydrates: 15g
- Protein: 25g

Directions:

- Heat the vegetable oil in a large pot over medium heat. Add the chopped onion and cook until softened, about 5 minutes.

- Add the minced garlic and thinly sliced red bell pepper to the pot. Cook for another 2-3 minutes until fragrant and softened.

- Stir in the Thai red curry paste and cook for 1 minute, stirring constantly to coat the vegetables.

- Pour in the coconut milk, chicken or vegetable broth, fish sauce, lime juice, and brown sugar. Stir well to combine and bring the mixture to a simmer.

- Add the sliced mushrooms to the pot and simmer for 5 minutes.

- Add the peeled and deveined shrimp to the pot and cook for 3-4 minutes, or until the shrimp are pink and cooked through.

- Stir in the baby spinach leaves and cook for another minute until wilted.

- Season the soup with salt and pepper to taste.

- Serve the Thai coconut curry soup hot, garnished with chopped fresh cilantro. Serve with cooked rice or rice noodles on the side.

Spinach and White Bean Soup

Soup

Cook time:
30 min

Prep time:
10 min

Servings:
4

Ingredients:

- 1 tablespoon (15ml) olive oil
- 1 onion, chopped
- 2 cloves garlic, minced
- 4 cups (960ml) vegetable broth (ensure it's gluten-free)
- 1 can (14 oz/400g) white beans, drained and rinsed
- 1 teaspoon (5g) dried thyme
- 1 teaspoon (5g) dried oregano
- 1/2 teaspoon (2.5g) paprika
- Salt and pepper, to taste
- 4 cups (120g) fresh spinach leaves
- Juice of 1 lemon
- **Optional toppings:** grated Parmesan cheese, red pepper flakes, chopped fresh parsley

Directions:

- In a large pot, heat the olive oil over medium heat. Add the chopped onion and cook until softened, about 5 minutes.

- Add the minced garlic to the pot and cook for another 1-2 minutes, until fragrant.

- Pour in the vegetable broth and bring to a simmer.

- Add the drained and rinsed white beans, dried thyme, dried oregano, and paprika to the pot. Stir well to combine.

- Season the soup with salt and pepper to taste. Allow the soup to simmer for 10-15 minutes to allow the flavors to meld together.

- Add the fresh spinach leaves to the pot and cook until wilted, about 2-3 minutes.

- Squeeze in the juice of one lemon and stir to combine.

- Taste and adjust the seasonings if necessary.

- Serve the spinach and white bean soup hot, garnished with grated Parmesan cheese, red pepper flakes, and chopped fresh parsley if desired.

Nutritional Value (Per Serving):

- Calories: Approximately 180 kcal
- Fat: 4g
- Cholesterol: 0mg
- Sodium: 800mg
- Carbohydrates: 28g
- Protein: 10g

Corn Chowder

Soup

Cook time:
40 min

Prep time:
15 min

Servings:
6

Ingredients:

- 4 slices bacon, chopped
- 1 onion, diced
- 2 cloves garlic, minced
- 3 cups (720ml) chicken or vegetable broth (ensure it's gluten-free)
- 3 cups (450g) fresh or frozen corn kernels
- 2 medium potatoes (about 300g), peeled and diced
- 1 red bell pepper, diced
- 1 teaspoon (5g) dried thyme
- 1/2 teaspoon (2.5g) smoked paprika
- Salt and pepper, to taste
- 1 cup (240ml) heavy cream
- 2 tablespoons (30ml) cornstarch mixed with 2 tablespoons (30ml) water
- **Optional toppings:** chopped fresh chives, grated cheddar cheese, crispy bacon bits

Nutritional Value (Per Serving):

- Calories: Approximately 350 kcal
- Fat: 20g
- Cholesterol: 50mg
- Sodium: 800mg
- Carbohydrates: 35g
- Protein: 10g

Directions:

- In a large pot or Dutch oven, cook the chopped bacon over medium heat until crisp. Remove the bacon from the pot and set aside, leaving the rendered fat in the pot.

- Add the diced onion to the pot and cook until softened, about 5 minutes.

- Add the minced garlic to the pot and cook for another minute until fragrant.

- Pour in the chicken or vegetable broth, scraping the bottom of the pot to release any browned bits.

- Add the corn kernels, diced potatoes, diced red bell pepper, dried thyme, and smoked paprika to the pot. Stir well to combine.

- Season the chowder with salt and pepper to taste. Bring the mixture to a simmer and cook for 20-25 minutes, or until the potatoes are tender.

- Stir in the heavy cream and bring the chowder back to a simmer.

- In a small bowl, mix the cornstarch with water to form a slurry. Gradually pour the slurry into the chowder while stirring continuously. Cook for another 5-10 minutes, or until the chowder has thickened slightly.

- Taste and adjust the seasonings if necessary.

Mushroom Soup with Thyme

Soup

Cook time:
30 min

Prep time:
10 min

Servings:
4

Ingredients:

- 2 tablespoons (30ml) olive oil
- 1 onion, chopped
- 2 cloves garlic, minced
- 1 lb (450g) mushrooms, sliced
- 4 cups (960ml) vegetable broth (ensure it's gluten-free)
- 1 teaspoon (5g) dried thyme
- Salt and pepper, to taste
- 1 cup (240ml) heavy cream
- Fresh thyme leaves, for garnish (optional)

Directions:

- In a large pot, heat the olive oil over medium heat. Add the chopped onion and cook until softened, about 5 minutes.

- Add the minced garlic to the pot and cook for another minute until fragrant.

- Add the sliced mushrooms to the pot and cook, stirring occasionally, until they release their moisture and start to brown, about 8-10 minutes.

- Pour in the vegetable broth and dried thyme. Stir well to combine.

- Bring the soup to a simmer and cook for another 10 minutes to allow the flavors to meld together.

- Season the soup with salt and pepper to taste.

- Use an immersion blender to blend the soup until smooth. Alternatively, carefully transfer the soup to a blender and blend in batches until smooth. Be cautious with hot liquids in a blender; work in batches and vent the lid.

- Stir in the heavy cream and simmer for another 2-3 minutes.

- Taste and adjust the seasonings if necessary.

- Serve the mushroom soup hot, garnished with fresh thyme leaves if desired.

Nutritional Value (Per Serving):

- Calories: Approximately 250 kcal
- Fat: 20g
- Cholesterol: 40mg
- Sodium: 700mg
- Carbohydrates: 15g
- Protein: 5g

Broccoli Cheddar Soup

Soup

Cook time:
30 min

Prep time:
15 min

Servings:
4

Ingredients:

- 2 tablespoons (28g) unsalted butter
- 1 onion, diced
- 2 cloves garlic, minced
- 4 cups (960ml) vegetable broth (ensure it's gluten-free)
- 1 lb (450g) broccoli florets, chopped
- 2 medium potatoes (about 300g), peeled and diced
- 1/4 cup (30g) gluten-free all-purpose flour
- 2 cups (480ml) milk (any type, dairy or plant-based)
- 2 cups (200g) shredded cheddar cheese
- Salt and pepper, to taste
- **Optional toppings:** additional shredded cheddar cheese, crumbled cooked bacon, chopped fresh chives

Directions:

- In a large pot, melt the unsalted butter over medium heat. Add the diced onion and cook until softened, about 5 minutes.

- Add the minced garlic to the pot and cook for another minute until fragrant.

- Stir in the vegetable broth, chopped broccoli florets, and diced potatoes. Bring the mixture to a simmer and cook for 15-20 minutes, or until the vegetables are tender.

- In a small bowl, whisk together the gluten-free all-purpose flour and milk until smooth. Gradually pour the mixture into the pot while stirring continuously.

- Cook the soup for another 5 minutes, stirring occasionally, until it thickens slightly.

- Reduce the heat to low and stir in the shredded cheddar cheese until melted and smooth.

- Season the soup with salt and pepper to taste.

- Taste and adjust the seasonings if necessary.

- Serve the broccoli cheddar soup hot, topped with additional shredded cheddar cheese, crumbled cooked bacon, and chopped fresh chives if desired.

Nutritional Value (Per Serving):

- Calories: Approximately 400 kcal
- Fat: 25g
- Cholesterol: 70mg
- Sodium: 900mg
- Carbohydrates: 30g
- Protein: 18g

Split Pea Soup with Ham

Soup

Cook time:
2 hr

Prep time:
15 min

Servings:
6

Ingredients:

- 2 tablespoons (30ml) olive oil
- 1 onion, chopped
- 2 carrots, diced
- 2 celery stalks, diced
- 2 cloves garlic, minced
- 1 lb (450g) dried split peas, rinsed and drained
- 8 cups (1920ml) water or vegetable broth (ensure it's gluten-free)
- 1 ham hock or 1 cup (150g) diced cooked ham
- 1 bay leaf
- 1 teaspoon (5g) dried thyme
- Salt and pepper, to taste
- **Optional garnish:** chopped fresh parsley

Directions:

- In a large pot or Dutch oven, heat the olive oil over medium heat. Add the chopped onion, diced carrots, and diced celery. Cook until the vegetables are softened, about 5-7 minutes.

- Add the minced garlic to the pot and cook for another minute until fragrant.

- Add the rinsed and drained dried split peas to the pot, along with the water or vegetable broth.

- Add the ham hock or diced cooked ham, bay leaf, and dried thyme to the pot. Stir well to combine.

- Bring the soup to a boil, then reduce the heat to low. Cover and simmer for 1.5 to 2 hours, stirring occasionally, until the split peas are tender and the soup has thickened.

- If using a ham hock, remove it from the soup and discard the bone. Shred any meat from the ham hock and return it to the soup. If using diced cooked ham, simply stir it into the soup.

- Season the split pea soup with salt and pepper to taste. Remove the bay leaf before serving.

- Ladle the split pea soup into bowls and garnish with chopped fresh parsley if desired.

Nutritional Value (Per Serving):

- Calories: Approximately 300 kcal
- Fat: 5g
- Cholesterol: 10mg
- Sodium: 800mg
- Carbohydrates: 45g
- Protein: 20g

Italian Wedding Soup

Soup

Cook time:
30 min

Prep time:
20 min

Servings:
6

Ingredients:

- 1 tablespoon (15ml) olive oil
- 1 onion, finely chopped
- 2 carrots, diced
- 2 celery stalks, diced
- 2 cloves garlic, minced
- 8 cups (1920ml) chicken broth (ensure it's gluten-free)
- 1 cup (100g) gluten-free breadcrumbs
- 1/4 cup (60ml) milk (any type, dairy or plant-based)
- 1 lb (450g) gluten-free ground chicken or turkey
- 1 egg, lightly beaten
- 2 tablespoons (30ml) chopped fresh parsley
- 1 teaspoon (5ml) dried oregano
- Salt and pepper, to taste
- 2 cups (60g) fresh spinach leaves
- Grated Parmesan cheese, for serving (optional)

Nutritional Value (Per Serving):

- Calories: Approximately 250 kcal
- Fat: 10g
- Cholesterol: 80mg
- Sodium: 1000mg
- Carbohydrates: 15g
- Protein: 25g

Directions:

- In a large pot, heat the olive oil over medium heat. Add the chopped onion, diced carrots, and diced celery. Cook until the vegetables are softened, about 5-7 minutes.

- Add the minced garlic to the pot and cook for another minute until fragrant.

- Pour in the chicken broth and bring to a simmer.

- In a medium bowl, combine the gluten-free breadcrumbs and milk. Let it sit for a few minutes to absorb the liquid.

- Add the ground chicken or turkey, beaten egg, chopped fresh parsley, dried oregano, salt, and pepper to the breadcrumb mixture. Mix until well combined.

- Shape the meat mixture into small meatballs, about 1 inch (2.5cm) in diameter.

- Carefully drop the meatballs into the simmering broth. Cook for 10-12 minutes, or until the meatballs are cooked through and no longer pink in the center.

- Stir in the fresh spinach leaves and cook for another 2-3 minutes, until wilted.

- Taste the soup and adjust the seasoning if necessary.

- Ladle the Italian wedding soup into bowls and serve hot, garnished with grated Parmesan cheese if desired.

Salad Recipes

Caprese Salad with Balsamic Glaze

Salad

Cook time:
0 min

Prep time:
10 min

Servings:
4

Ingredients:

- 2 large ripe tomatoes, sliced (about 400g)
- 1 ball fresh mozzarella cheese, sliced (about 200g)
- Fresh basil leaves
- Salt and pepper, to taste
- 2 tablespoons (30ml) balsamic glaze
- 1 tablespoon (15ml) extra virgin olive oil

Directions:

- Arrange the sliced tomatoes and mozzarella cheese alternately on a serving platter.

- Tuck fresh basil leaves between the tomato and mozzarella slices.

- Season the salad with salt and pepper to taste.

- Drizzle the balsamic glaze and extra virgin olive oil over the salad.

Nutritional Value (Per Serving):

- Calories: Approximately 190 kcal
- Fat: 14g
- Cholesterol: 25mg
- Sodium: 250mg
- Carbohydrates: 7g
- Protein: 10g

Greek Salad with Feta and Olives

Salad

Cook time:
0 min

Prep time:
15 min

Servings:
4

Ingredients:

- 2 large ripe tomatoes, diced (about 400g)
- 1 cucumber, diced (about 300g)
- 1 red onion, thinly sliced
- 1/2 cup (75g) Kalamata olives, pitted
- 4 ounces (120g) feta cheese, crumbled
- 1/4 cup (60ml) extra virgin olive oil
- 2 tablespoons (30ml) red wine vinegar
- 1 teaspoon (5ml) dried oregano
- Salt and pepper, to taste
- Fresh parsley, chopped, for garnish (optional)

Directions:

- In a large mixing bowl, combine the diced tomatoes, diced cucumber, sliced red onion, and Kalamata olives.

- In a small bowl, whisk together the extra virgin olive oil, red wine vinegar, dried oregano, salt, and pepper to make the dressing.

- Pour the dressing over the salad ingredients in the mixing bowl. Toss gently to coat everything evenly with the dressing.

- Transfer the salad to a serving platter or individual plates.

- Sprinkle the crumbled feta cheese over the top of the salad.

- Garnish with chopped fresh parsley, if desired.

Nutritional Value (Per Serving):

- Calories: Approximately 280 kcal
- Fat: 22g
- Cholesterol: 25mg
- Sodium: 650mg
- Carbohydrates: 12g
- Protein: 7g

Quinoa Salad with Roasted Vegetables

Salad

Cook time:
30 min

Prep time:
15 min

Servings:
4

Ingredients:

- 1 cup (180g) quinoa, rinsed
- 2 cups (480ml) water
- 1 red bell pepper, diced
- 1 yellow bell pepper, diced
- 1 zucchini, diced
- 1 small red onion, thinly sliced
- 2 tablespoons (30ml) olive oil
- Salt and pepper, to taste
- 1/4 cup (30g) crumbled feta cheese
- 2 tablespoons (30ml) balsamic vinegar
- Fresh parsley, chopped, for garnish (optional)

Directions:

- Preheat the oven to 400°F (200°C).

- In a medium saucepan, combine the rinsed quinoa and water. Bring to a boil, then reduce the heat to low, cover, and simmer for 15 minutes, or until the quinoa is tender and the water is absorbed. Remove from heat and let it sit, covered, for 5 minutes. Fluff with a fork and set aside.

- While the quinoa is cooking, spread the diced red bell pepper, yellow bell pepper, zucchini, and red onion on a baking sheet. Drizzle with olive oil and season with salt and pepper. Toss to coat the vegetables evenly with oil and seasoning.

- Roast the vegetables in the preheated oven for 15-20 minutes, or until they are tender and slightly caramelized, stirring halfway through cooking.

- In a large mixing bowl, combine the cooked quinoa and roasted vegetables.

- Add the crumbled feta cheese and balsamic vinegar to the bowl. Toss gently to combine all ingredients.

- Garnish with chopped fresh parsley, if desired.

- Serve the quinoa salad warm or at room temperature.

Nutritional Value (Per Serving):

- Calories: Approximately 280 kcal
- Fat: 22g
- Cholesterol: 25mg
- Sodium: 650mg
- Carbohydrates: 12g
- Protein: 7g

Spinach Strawberry Salad with Balsamic Vinaigrette

Salad

Cook time:
0 min

Prep time:
10 min

Servings:
4

Ingredients:

- 6 cups (180g) fresh spinach leaves
- 1 cup (150g) fresh strawberries, hulled and sliced
- 1/4 cup (30g) sliced almonds
- 2 tablespoons (30ml) balsamic vinegar
- 2 tablespoons (30ml) extra virgin olive oil
- 1 teaspoon (5ml) honey (optional)
- Salt and pepper, to taste

Directions:

- In a large mixing bowl, combine the fresh spinach leaves, sliced strawberries, and sliced almonds.

- In a small bowl, whisk together the balsamic vinegar, extra virgin olive oil, honey (if using), salt, and pepper to make the vinaigrette.

- Pour the balsamic vinaigrette over the salad ingredients in the mixing bowl.

- Toss gently to coat the salad evenly with the dressing.

- Serve the spinach strawberry salad immediately.

Nutritional Value (Per Serving):

- Calories: Approximately 120 kcal
- Fat: 9g
- Cholesterol: 0mg
- Sodium: 50mg
- Carbohydrates: 9g
- Protein: 3g

Cobb Salad (without Croutons)

Salad

Cook time:
0 min

Prep time:
20 min

Servings:
4

Ingredients:

- 8 cups (320g) mixed salad greens (such as romaine lettuce, spinach, and arugula)
- 2 cups (300g) cooked chicken breast, diced
- 4 hard-boiled eggs, sliced
- 1 large avocado, diced
- 1 cup (150g) cherry tomatoes, halved
- 1/2 cup (75g) crumbled blue cheese
- 4 slices cooked bacon, crumbled
- 1/4 cup (60ml) balsamic vinaigrette or your favorite salad dressing

Directions:

- Arrange the mixed salad greens on a large serving platter or individual plates.

- Top the greens with the diced cooked chicken breast, sliced hard-boiled eggs, diced avocado, halved cherry tomatoes, crumbled blue cheese, and crumbled bacon.

- Drizzle the balsamic vinaigrette or your preferred salad dressing over the salad.

- Serve the Cobb salad immediately.

Nutritional Value (Per Serving):

- Calories: Approximately 420 kcal
- Fat: 28g
- Cholesterol: 250mg
- Sodium: 650mg
- Carbohydrates: 9g
- Protein: 34g

Avocado Tomato Salad with Lime Dressing

Salad

Cook time:
0 min

Prep time:
10 min

Servings:
4

Ingredients:

- 2 ripe avocados, diced (about 300g)
- 2 large tomatoes, diced (about 400g)
- 1/4 cup (15g) fresh cilantro, chopped
- 1/4 cup (60ml) lime juice
- 2 tablespoons (30ml) extra virgin olive oil
- 1 teaspoon (5ml) honey (optional)
- Salt and pepper, to taste
- Red pepper flakes, for garnish (optional)

Directions:

- In a large mixing bowl, combine the diced avocados, diced tomatoes, and chopped cilantro.

- In a small bowl, whisk together the lime juice, extra virgin olive oil, honey (if using), salt, and pepper to make the dressing.

- Pour the lime dressing over the avocado and tomato mixture in the mixing bowl.

- Gently toss to coat all ingredients evenly with the dressing.

- Garnish with a sprinkle of red pepper flakes, if desired.

- Serve the avocado tomato salad immediately.

Nutritional Value (Per Serving):

- Calories: Approximately 220 kcal
- Fat: 19g
- Cholesterol: 0mg
- Sodium: 10mg
- Carbohydrates: 12g
- Protein: 3g

Caesar Salad

Salad

Cook time:
0 min

Prep time:
15 min

Servings:
4

Ingredients:

- 1 large head of romaine lettuce, washed and chopped (about 400g)
- 1/2 cup (60g) grated Parmesan cheese
- 1/2 cup (120ml) gluten-free Caesar salad dressing
- 1/2 cup (50g) gluten-free croutons (optional, or omit for gluten-free)
- Salt and pepper, to taste

Directions:

- In a large mixing bowl, combine the chopped romaine lettuce and grated Parmesan cheese.

- Add the gluten-free Caesar salad dressing to the bowl.

- Toss the salad gently until all the lettuce leaves are coated evenly with the dressing.

- If using gluten-free croutons, add them to the salad and toss again to distribute.

- Season the salad with salt and pepper to taste.

- Serve the Caesar salad immediately as a delicious side dish or a light meal.

Nutritional Value (Per Serving):

- Calories: Approximately 220 kcal
- Fat: 18g
- Cholesterol: 10mg
- Sodium: 450mg
- Carbohydrates: 8g
- Protein: 5g

Beet and Goat Cheese Salad with Walnuts

Salad

Cook time:
45 min

Prep time:
15 min

Servings:
4

Ingredients:

- 4 medium beets, peeled and diced (about 500g)
- 4 cups (120g) mixed salad greens
- 4 ounces (115g) goat cheese, crumbled
- 1/2 cup (60g) walnuts, chopped
- 2 tablespoons (30ml) balsamic vinegar
- 2 tablespoons (30ml) extra virgin olive oil
- Salt and pepper, to taste

Directions:

- Preheat the oven to 400°F (200°C).

- Place the diced beets on a baking sheet and drizzle with olive oil. Season with salt and pepper.

- Roast the beets in the preheated oven for 40-45 minutes, or until they are tender when pierced with a fork. Remove from the oven and let cool slightly.

- In a large mixing bowl, combine the mixed salad greens, roasted beets, crumbled goat cheese, and chopped walnuts.

- In a small bowl, whisk together the balsamic vinegar and extra virgin olive oil to make the dressing.

- Drizzle the dressing over the salad and toss gently to coat all ingredients evenly.

- Divide the salad into serving bowls or plates.

- Serve the beet and goat cheese salad immediately.

Nutritional Value (Per Serving):

- Calories: Approximately 280 kcal
- Fat: 20g
- Cholesterol: 15mg
- Sodium: 220mg
- Carbohydrates: 20g
- Protein: 10g

Asian Cucumber Salad with Sesame Dressing

Salad

Cook time:
0 min

Prep time:
10 min

Servings:
4

Ingredients:

- 2 large cucumbers, thinly sliced (about 400g)
- 2 tablespoons (30ml) rice vinegar
- 1 tablespoon (15ml) soy sauce (gluten-free if needed)
- 1 tablespoon (15ml) sesame oil
- 1 teaspoon (5g) honey or maple syrup (optional)
- 1 tablespoon (15g) sesame seeds, toasted
- 2 green onions, thinly sliced
- Red pepper flakes, to taste (optional)
- Fresh cilantro leaves, for garnish (optional)

Directions:

- In a large mixing bowl, combine the thinly sliced cucumbers, rice vinegar, soy sauce, sesame oil, and honey (if using).

- Toss the cucumbers gently to coat them evenly with the dressing.

- Sprinkle the toasted sesame seeds over the cucumber mixture.

- Add the sliced green onions to the bowl and toss again to combine.

- If desired, add red pepper flakes for a hint of heat.

- Garnish with fresh cilantro leaves, if desired.

- Serve the Asian cucumber salad immediately as a refreshing side dish or appetizer.

Nutritional Value (Per Serving):

- Calories: Approximately 50 kcal
- Fat: 3g
- Cholesterol: 0mg
- Sodium: 150mg
- Carbohydrates: 5g
- Protein: 2g

Kale Salad with Apples and Pecans

Salad

Cook time:
0 min

Prep time:
15 min

Servings:
4

Ingredients:

- 1 bunch kale, stems removed and leaves chopped (about 200g)
- 1 large apple, thinly sliced (about 200g)
- 1/2 cup (60g) pecans, chopped
- 1/4 cup (60ml) olive oil
- 2 tablespoons (30ml) apple cider vinegar
- 1 tablespoon (15ml) honey or maple syrup
- Salt and pepper, to taste
- 1/4 cup (30g) crumbled feta cheese (optional)

Directions:

- In a large mixing bowl, add the chopped kale leaves, sliced apples, and chopped pecans.

- In a small bowl, whisk together the olive oil, apple cider vinegar, honey or maple syrup, salt, and pepper to make the dressing.

- Pour the dressing over the kale salad ingredients.

- Using clean hands, massage the dressing into the kale leaves for about 2-3 minutes. This helps to soften the kale and infuse it with flavor.

- Let the salad sit for about 5 minutes to allow the flavors to meld together.

- If desired, sprinkle crumbled feta cheese over the salad before serving.

- Serve the kale salad with apples and pecans as a nutritious side dish or light meal.

Nutritional Value (Per Serving):

- Calories: Approximately 250 kcal
- Fat: 19g
- Cholesterol: 0mg
- Sodium: 100mg
- Carbohydrates: 20g
- Protein: 4g

Tuna Salad with Mixed Greens

 Salad

 Cook time: 0 min

 Prep time: 10 min

 Servings: 2

Ingredients:

- 2 cans (150g each) tuna in water, drained
- 4 cups (120g) mixed salad greens
- 1/4 cup (60ml) olive oil
- 2 tablespoons (30ml) lemon juice
- 1 teaspoon (5ml) Dijon mustard
- Salt and pepper, to taste
- 1/4 cup (30g) sliced cucumber
- 1/4 cup (30g) cherry tomatoes, halved
- 1/4 cup (30g) sliced bell peppers
- 1/4 cup (30g) sliced red onion
- 2 tablespoons (30g) sliced black olives (optional)
- Fresh herbs, for garnish (optional)

Directions:

- In a large mixing bowl, combine the drained tuna, mixed salad greens, sliced cucumber, cherry tomatoes, sliced bell peppers, sliced red onion, and black olives (if using).

- In a small bowl, whisk together the olive oil, lemon juice, Dijon mustard, salt, and pepper to make the dressing.

- Pour the dressing over the tuna and vegetable mixture.

- Toss the salad gently until all ingredients are well coated with the dressing.

- Divide the tuna salad into serving bowls.

- Garnish with fresh herbs, if desired.

- Serve immediately as a satisfying and nutritious meal.

Nutritional Value (Per Serving):

- Calories: Approximately 320 kcal
- Fat: 22g
- Cholesterol: 35mg
- Sodium: 420mg
- Carbohydrates: 7g
- Protein: 25g

Mediterranean Chickpea Salad

Salad

Cook time:
0 min

Prep time:
15 min

Servings:
4

Ingredients:

- 2 cans (400g each) chickpeas, drained and rinsed
- 1 cup (150g) cherry tomatoes, halved
- 1 cucumber, diced
- 1/2 red onion, thinly sliced
- 1/4 cup (30g) Kalamata olives, pitted and halved
- 1/4 cup (30g) crumbled feta cheese
- 2 tablespoons (30ml) extra virgin olive oil
- 1 tablespoon (15ml) red wine vinegar
- 1 teaspoon (5ml) lemon juice
- 1 clove garlic, minced
- 1 teaspoon (5g) dried oregano
- Salt and pepper, to taste
- Fresh parsley, chopped, for garnish

Directions:

- In a large mixing bowl, combine the chickpeas, cherry tomatoes, diced cucumber, sliced red onion, Kalamata olives, and crumbled feta cheese.

- In a small bowl, whisk together the extra virgin olive oil, red wine vinegar, lemon juice, minced garlic, dried oregano, salt, and pepper to make the dressing.

- Pour the dressing over the chickpea salad mixture.

- Toss the salad gently until all ingredients are well coated with the dressing.

- Taste and adjust seasoning if needed.

- Garnish with chopped fresh parsley.

- Serve the Mediterranean chickpea salad immediately as a side dish or light meal.

Nutritional Value (Per Serving):

- Calories: Approximately 280 kcal
- Fat: 12g
- Cholesterol: 5mg
- Sodium: 480mg
- Carbohydrates: 33g
- Protein: 10g

Arugula Salad with Parmesan Shavings

Salad

Cook time:
0 min

Prep time:
10 min

Servings:
4

Ingredients:

- 6 cups (180g) arugula leaves
- 1/4 cup (30g) shaved Parmesan cheese
- 2 tablespoons (30ml) extra virgin olive oil
- 1 tablespoon (15ml) balsamic vinegar
- 1 teaspoon (5ml) honey
- Salt and pepper, to taste

Directions:

- In a large mixing bowl, add the arugula leaves.

- In a small bowl, whisk together the extra virgin olive oil, balsamic vinegar, honey, salt, and pepper to make the dressing.

- Pour the dressing over the arugula leaves.

- Toss the salad gently until all leaves are well coated with the dressing.

- Divide the dressed arugula onto serving plates.

- Top each serving with shaved Parmesan cheese.

- Serve the arugula salad with Parmesan shavings immediately as a refreshing appetizer or side dish.

Nutritional Value (Per Serving):

- Calories: Approximately 90 kcal
- Fat: 7g
- Cholesterol: 5mg
- Sodium: 120mg
- Carbohydrates: 3g
- Protein: 3g

Mexican Corn Salad with Avocado

 Salad

 Cook time:
10 min

 Prep time:
15 min

 Servings:
4

Ingredients:

- 4 ears of corn (about 400g), husked and kernels removed
- 1 avocado, diced
- 1/4 cup (30g) red onion, finely chopped
- 1/4 cup (30g) fresh cilantro, chopped
- 1 jalapeño pepper, seeded and minced
- Juice of 1 lime
- 2 tablespoons (30ml) extra virgin olive oil
- Salt and pepper, to taste
- 1/4 teaspoon (1.25ml) chili powder
- 1/4 teaspoon (1.25ml) cumin powder
- 1/4 cup (30g) crumbled feta cheese (optional)
- Lime wedges, for serving

Directions:

- In a large bowl, combine the corn kernels, diced avocado, chopped red onion, minced jalapeño pepper, and chopped cilantro.

- In a small bowl, whisk together the lime juice, extra virgin olive oil, salt, pepper, chili powder, and cumin powder to make the dressing.

- Pour the dressing over the corn salad mixture.

- Toss the salad gently until all ingredients are well coated with the dressing.

- Taste and adjust seasoning if needed.

- If desired, sprinkle crumbled feta cheese over the salad and toss lightly.

- Serve the Mexican corn salad with avocado immediately, garnished with lime wedges.

Nutritional Value (Per Serving):

- Calories: Approximately 210 kcal
- Fat: 14g
- Cholesterol: 0mg
- Sodium: 180mg
- Carbohydrates: 21g
- Protein: 4g

Waldorf Salad with Grapes and Walnuts

Salad

Cook time:
0 min

Prep time:
15 min

Servings:
4

Ingredients:

- 2 cups (200g) diced apples
- 1 cup (150g) seedless grapes, halved
- 1/2 cup (60g) chopped celery
- 1/2 cup (60g) chopped walnuts
- 1/4 cup (60ml) mayonnaise
- 2 tablespoons (30ml) Greek yogurt
- 1 tablespoon (15ml) lemon juice
- 1 tablespoon (15ml) honey
- Salt and pepper, to taste
- Lettuce leaves, for serving (optional)

Directions:

- In a large mixing bowl, combine the diced apples, halved grapes, chopped celery, and chopped walnuts.

- In a small bowl, whisk together the mayonnaise, Greek yogurt, lemon juice, honey, salt, and pepper to make the dressing.

- Pour the dressing over the apple, grape, celery, and walnut mixture.

- Toss the salad gently until all ingredients are well coated with the dressing.

- Taste and adjust seasoning if needed.

- If desired, arrange lettuce leaves on serving plates and spoon the Waldorf salad over the lettuce.

- Serve the Waldorf salad with grapes and walnuts immediately as a refreshing side dish or light meal.

Nutritional Value (Per Serving):

- Calories: Approximately 250 kcal
- Fat: 18g
- Cholesterol: 5mg
- Sodium: 150mg
- Carbohydrates: 21g
- Protein: 4g

Main Dishes

Baked Salmon with Garlic Butter and Steamed Asparagus

Main dishes

Cook time:
20 min

Prep time:
10 min

Servings:
4

Ingredients:

For the Salmon:
- 4 salmon fillets (about 170g each)
- 2 tablespoons (30ml) olive oil
- Salt and pepper to taste
- 2 cloves garlic, minced
- 2 tablespoons (28g) unsalted butter, melted
- 1 tablespoon (15ml) freshly squeezed lemon juice
- 1 tablespoon (15ml) chopped fresh parsley

For the Asparagus:
- 1 bunch asparagus, woody ends trimmed
- 1 tablespoon (15ml) olive oil
- Salt and pepper to taste

Directions:

- Preheat your oven to 375°F (190°C).

- Place the salmon fillets on a baking sheet lined with parchment paper. Drizzle the salmon with olive oil and season with salt and pepper.

- In a small bowl, combine the minced garlic, melted butter, lemon juice, and chopped parsley. Brush the garlic butter mixture over the salmon fillets, coating them evenly.

- Bake the salmon in the preheated oven for 12-15 minutes, or until the fish flakes easily with a fork and is cooked through.

- While the salmon is baking, prepare the asparagus. Steam the asparagus until crisp-tender, about 5-7 minutes, depending on the thickness of the spears.

- Once the asparagus is steamed, transfer it to a serving platter. Drizzle with olive oil and season with salt and pepper to taste.

- Remove the baked salmon from the oven and serve it immediately with the steamed asparagus.

Nutritional Value (Per Serving):

- Calories: Approximately 340 kcal
- Fat: 22g
- Cholesterol: 90mg
- Sodium: 200mg
- Carbohydrates: 4g
- Protein: 32g

Beef Stir-Fry with Bell Peppers and Rice Noodles

Main dishes

Cook time:
20 min

Prep time:
15 min

Servings:
4

Ingredients:

For the Stir-Fry:
- 1 lb (450g) flank steak, thinly sliced against the grain
- 8 oz (225g) rice noodles
- 2 bell peppers (1 red, 1 green), thinly sliced
- 1 medium onion, thinly sliced
- 2 cloves garlic, minced
- 2 tablespoons (30ml) vegetable oil
- Salt and pepper to taste
- Sesame seeds for garnish (optional)
- Chopped green onions for garnish (optional)

For the Sauce:
- 1/4 cup (60ml) gluten-free soy sauce
- 2 tablespoons (30ml) rice vinegar
- 1 tablespoon (15ml) honey
- 1 tablespoon (15ml) sesame oil
- 1 teaspoon (5ml) freshly grated ginger
- 1 teaspoon (5ml) cornstarch mixed with 2 teaspoons (10ml) water

Directions:

- Cook the rice noodles according to the package instructions. Drain and set aside.

- In a small bowl, whisk together the ingredients for the sauce: gluten-free soy sauce, rice vinegar, honey, sesame oil, grated ginger, and cornstarch mixture. Set aside.

- Heat 1 tablespoon of vegetable oil in a large skillet or wok over medium-high heat. Add the thinly sliced flank steak and season with salt and pepper. Stir-fry for 3-4 minutes until browned. Remove the beef from the skillet and set aside.

- In the same skillet, add another tablespoon of vegetable oil. Add the sliced bell peppers and onion. Stir-fry for 3-4 minutes until they start to soften.

- Add the minced garlic to the skillet and cook for an additional 30 seconds until fragrant.

- Return the cooked beef to the skillet. Pour the prepared sauce over the beef and vegetables. Stir well to coat everything evenly.

- Add the cooked rice noodles to the skillet and toss everything together until the noodles are well coated with the sauce.

- Cook for another 2-3 minutes, allowing the flavors to meld together and the noodles to absorb the sauce.

- Once everything is heated through, remove the skillet from the heat.

- Serve the beef stir-fry with rice noodles hot, garnished with sesame seeds and chopped green onions if desired.

Nutritional Value (Per Serving):

- Calories: Approximately 450 kcal
- Fat: 14g
- Cholesterol: 45mg
- Sodium: 800mg
- Carbohydrates: 60g
- Protein: 24g

Quinoa Stuffed Bell Peppers with Tomato Sauce

Main dishes

Cook time:
45 min

Prep time:
20 min

Servings:
4

Ingredients:

For the Stuffed Bell Peppers:
- 4 large bell peppers (any color), halved and seeds removed
- 1 cup (185g) quinoa, rinsed
- 2 cups (480ml) vegetable broth
- 1 tablespoon (15ml) olive oil
- 1 small onion, finely chopped
- 2 cloves garlic, minced
- 1 cup (150g) cherry tomatoes, halved
- 1 cup (150g) cooked black beans (canned is fine)
- 1/2 cup (75g) corn kernels (fresh, canned, or frozen)
- 1 teaspoon (5ml) ground cumin
- 1 teaspoon (5ml) paprika
- Salt and pepper to taste
- Fresh parsley or cilantro, chopped, for garnish

For the Tomato Sauce:
- 1 can (14 oz / 400g) diced tomatoes
- 2 cloves garlic, minced
- 1 teaspoon (5ml) dried oregano
- Salt and pepper to taste

Nutritional Value (Per Serving):
- Calories: Approximately 320 kcal
- Fat: 6g
- Cholesterol: 0mg
- Sodium: 670mg
- Carbohydrates: 58g
- Protein: 11g

Directions:

- Preheat the oven to 375°F (190°C). Lightly grease a baking dish large enough to fit the bell pepper halves.

- In a medium saucepan, bring the vegetable broth to a boil. Add the quinoa, reduce the heat to low, cover, and simmer for 15-20 minutes, or until the quinoa is cooked and the liquid is absorbed. Remove from heat and fluff with a fork.

- While the quinoa is cooking, heat the olive oil in a large skillet over medium heat. Add the chopped onion and cook until softened, about 3-4 minutes. Add the minced garlic and cook for an additional 1-2 minutes.

- Add the cherry tomatoes, black beans, and corn to the skillet. Stir in the cooked quinoa, ground cumin, paprika, salt, and pepper. Cook for another 3-4 minutes, allowing the flavors to blend. Remove from heat.

- In a separate saucepan, combine the diced tomatoes, minced garlic, dried oregano, salt, and pepper for the tomato sauce. Bring to a simmer over medium heat and cook for 5-7 minutes, stirring occasionally, until slightly thickened.

- Place the bell pepper halves in the prepared baking dish, cut side up. Spoon the quinoa mixture evenly into each bell pepper half, pressing gently to pack it in.

- Pour the tomato sauce over the stuffed bell peppers, covering them evenly.

- Cover the baking dish with foil and bake in the preheated oven for 25-30 minutes, or until the bell peppers are tender.

- Once cooked, remove the foil and bake for an additional 5-10 minutes, or until the tops are slightly golden.

- Remove from the oven and let cool for a few minutes before serving. Garnish with fresh parsley or cilantro if desired.

Shrimp Tacos with Corn Tortillas and Avocado Salsa

Main dishes

Cook time:
15 min

Prep time:
20 min

Servings:
4

Ingredients:

For the Shrimp:
- 1 pound (450g) large shrimp, peeled and deveined
- 1 tablespoon (15ml) olive oil
- 1 teaspoon (5ml) chili powder
- 1/2 teaspoon (2.5ml) cumin
- Salt and pepper to taste

For the Avocado Salsa:
- 2 ripe avocados, diced
- 1 small red onion, finely chopped
- 1 jalapeño pepper, seeded and finely chopped
- 1/4 cup (15g) fresh cilantro, chopped
- Juice of 2 limes
- Salt to taste

For Serving:
- 8 corn tortillas, warmed
- Shredded lettuce
- Sliced radishes
- Lime wedges
- Additional cilantro for garnish

Directions:

- In a medium bowl, toss the shrimp with olive oil, chili powder, cumin, salt, and pepper until evenly coated.

- Heat a large skillet over medium-high heat. Add the seasoned shrimp and cook for 2-3 minutes per side, or until pink and cooked through. Remove from heat and set aside.

- In a separate bowl, combine diced avocados, chopped red onion, jalapeño pepper, cilantro, lime juice, and salt. Gently toss to combine.

- To assemble the tacos, place a spoonful of avocado salsa on each warm corn tortilla. Top with cooked shrimp, shredded lettuce, sliced radishes, and additional cilantro if desired.

- Serve the shrimp tacos immediately with lime wedges on the side for squeezing.

Nutritional Value (Per Serving):

- Calories: Approximately 380 kcal
- Fat: 17g
- Cholesterol: 195mg
- Sodium: 410mg
- Carbohydrates: 33g
- Protein: 28g

Spaghetti Squash with Marinara Sauce and Meatballs

Main dishes

Cook time:
1 hr

Prep time:
20 min

Servings:
4

Ingredients:

For the Spaghetti Squash:
- 1 medium spaghetti squash (about 2 pounds / 900g)
- 2 tablespoons (30ml) olive oil
- Salt and pepper to taste

For the Marinara Sauce:
- 2 tablespoons (30ml) olive oil
- 2 cloves garlic, minced
- 1 can (14 ounces / 400g) crushed tomatoes
- 1 teaspoon (5ml) dried oregano
- 1 teaspoon (5ml) dried basil
- Salt and pepper to taste

For the Meatballs:
- 1 pound (450g) ground beef
- 1/4 cup (25g) grated Parmesan cheese
- 1/4 cup (30g) gluten-free breadcrumbs
- 1 egg
- 2 cloves garlic, minced
- 1 teaspoon (5ml) dried oregano
- Salt and pepper to taste

For Serving:
- Fresh basil leaves, chopped
- Grated Parmesan cheese

Nutritional Value (Per Serving):

- Calories: Approximately 420 kcal
- Fat: 25g
- Cholesterol: 120mg
- Sodium: 630mg
- Carbohydrates: 18g
- Protein: 32g

Directions:

- Preheat the oven to 400°F (200°C). Line a baking sheet with parchment paper.

- Cut the spaghetti squash in half lengthwise and scoop out the seeds. Brush the cut sides with olive oil and season with salt and pepper. Place the squash halves cut-side down on the prepared baking sheet. Bake for 40-45 minutes, or until the squash is tender and easily pierced with a fork. Remove from the oven and let cool slightly.

- While the squash is baking, prepare the marinara sauce. Heat olive oil in a saucepan over medium heat. Add the minced garlic and cook for 1-2 minutes, or until fragrant. Stir in the crushed tomatoes, dried oregano, dried basil, salt, and pepper. Simmer the sauce for 15-20 minutes, stirring occasionally, until thickened.

- To make the meatballs, combine the ground beef, grated Parmesan cheese, gluten-free breadcrumbs, egg, minced garlic, dried oregano, salt, and pepper in a bowl. Mix until well combined. Shape the mixture into small meatballs.

- Heat a skillet over medium heat and add a bit of olive oil. Add the meatballs to the skillet and cook for 8-10 minutes, turning occasionally, until browned on all sides and cooked through.

- Once the spaghetti squash is cool enough to handle, use a fork to scrape the flesh into "spaghetti" strands. Divide the spaghetti squash among serving plates.

- Top the spaghetti squash with marinara sauce and meatballs. Garnish with chopped fresh basil leaves and grated Parmesan cheese.

Thai Green Curry with Chicken and Jasmine Rice

Main dishes

Cook time:
30 min

Prep time:
15 min

Servings:
4

Ingredients:

For the Thai Green Curry Paste:
- 2 stalks lemongrass, white parts only, chopped
- 4 cloves garlic, peeled
- 1 shallot, peeled and chopped
- 1-inch (2.5cm) piece of ginger, peeled and chopped
- 2 green Thai chilies, chopped
- 1 tablespoon (15ml) fish sauce
- 1 tablespoon (15ml) lime juice
- 1 tablespoon (15ml) olive oil

For the Curry:
- 1 tablespoon (15ml) olive oil
- 1 pound (450g) boneless, skinless chicken breast, thinly sliced
- 1 red bell pepper, sliced
- 1 green bell pepper, sliced
- 1 cup (240ml) coconut milk
- 1 cup (240ml) chicken broth
- 2 tablespoons (30ml) gluten-free soy sauce
- 1 tablespoon (15ml) brown sugar
- 1 cup (180g) bamboo shoots, drained
- 1 cup (180g) baby corn, drained
- Salt and pepper to taste
- Fresh basil leaves, chopped, for garnish
- Cooked jasmine rice, for serving

Directions:

- In a food processor or blender, combine all the ingredients for the Thai green curry paste. Blend until smooth.

- Heat olive oil in a large skillet or wok over medium heat. Add the sliced chicken breast and cook until lightly browned, about 5-6 minutes.

- Add the sliced bell peppers to the skillet and cook for an additional 2-3 minutes, until slightly softened.

- Stir in the prepared green curry paste and cook for 1-2 minutes, stirring constantly, until fragrant.

- Pour in the coconut milk, chicken broth, gluten-free soy sauce, and brown sugar. Stir to combine.

- Add the bamboo shoots and baby corn to the skillet. Season with salt and pepper to taste. Bring the curry to a simmer and cook for 10-15 minutes, or until the chicken is cooked through and the vegetables are tender.

- Serve the Thai green curry hot over cooked jasmine rice. Garnish with chopped fresh basil leaves.

Nutritional Value (Per Serving):

- Calories: Approximately 420 kcal
- Fat: 22g
- Cholesterol: 80mg
- Sodium: 950mg
- Carbohydrates: 26g
- Protein: 30g

Baked Pork Chops with Mashed Potatoes and Green Beans

Main dishes

Cook time:
1 hr

Prep time:
20 min

Servings:
4

Ingredients:

For the Pork Chops:
- 4 bone-in pork chops (about 6 ounces each) [170g]
- 2 tablespoons (30ml) olive oil
- 1 teaspoon (5g) garlic powder
- 1 teaspoon (5g) onion powder
- 1 teaspoon (5g) paprika
- Salt and pepper to taste

For the Mashed Potatoes:
- 4 large potatoes, peeled and cubed
- 1/2 cup (120ml) milk
- 2 tablespoons (28g) butter
- Salt and pepper to taste

For the Green Beans:
- 1 pound (450g) fresh green beans, trimmed
- 2 tablespoons (30ml) olive oil
- 2 cloves garlic, minced
- Salt and pepper to taste

Nutritional Value (Per Serving):

- Calories: Approximately 550 kcal
- Fat: 26g
- Cholesterol: 120mg
- Sodium: 240mg
- Carbohydrates: 45g
- Protein: 38g

Directions:

- Preheat the oven to 375°F (190°C).

- In a small bowl, mix together the garlic powder, onion powder, paprika, salt, and pepper. Rub the pork chops with olive oil and then coat them evenly with the spice mixture.

- Place the seasoned pork chops on a baking sheet lined with parchment paper. Bake in the preheated oven for 25-30 minutes, or until the internal temperature reaches 145°F (63°C) using a meat thermometer.

- While the pork chops are baking, prepare the mashed potatoes. Place the cubed potatoes in a pot of salted water and bring to a boil. Cook until tender, about 15-20 minutes. Drain the potatoes and return them to the pot.

- Add the milk and butter to the pot with the potatoes. Mash until smooth and creamy. Season with salt and pepper to taste.

- In a large skillet, heat olive oil over medium heat. Add the minced garlic and sauté for 1-2 minutes, until fragrant. Add the green beans to the skillet and cook for 5-7 minutes, stirring occasionally, until tender-crisp. Season with salt and pepper to taste.

- Serve the baked pork chops hot alongside the mashed potatoes and green beans.

Vegetable Stir-Fry with Tofu and Gluten-Free Soy Sauce

Main dishes

Cook time:
15 min

Prep time:
15 min

Servings:
4

Ingredients:

For the Stir-Fry:
- 14 ounces (400g) extra firm tofu, drained and cubed
- 2 tablespoons (30ml) gluten-free soy sauce
- 2 tablespoons (30ml) sesame oil
- 1 tablespoon (15ml) olive oil
- 2 cloves garlic, minced
- 1 teaspoon (5g) grated ginger
- 1 red bell pepper, sliced
- 1 yellow bell pepper, sliced
- 1 cup (150g) snow peas, trimmed
- 1 cup (100g) sliced mushrooms
- 1 medium carrot, julienned
- 2 green onions, chopped
- Sesame seeds, for garnish (optional)
- Cooked rice or noodles, for serving (optional)

For the Sauce:
- 3 tablespoons (45ml) gluten-free soy sauce
- 2 tablespoons (30ml) rice vinegar
- 1 tablespoon (15ml) honey or maple syrup
- 1 teaspoon (5ml) sesame oil
- 1 teaspoon (5g) cornstarch

Nutritional Value (Per Serving):

- Calories: Approximately 280 kcal
- Fat: 16g
- Cholesterol: 0mg
- Sodium: 800mg
- Carbohydrates: 20g
- Protein: 18g

Directions:

- In a medium bowl, toss the cubed tofu with 2 tablespoons of gluten-free soy sauce. Let it marinate for 10-15 minutes.

- In a small bowl, whisk together all the ingredients for the sauce: gluten-free soy sauce, rice vinegar, honey or maple syrup, sesame oil, and cornstarch. Set aside.

- Heat olive oil in a large skillet or wok over medium-high heat. Add the marinated tofu cubes and cook until golden brown on all sides, about 5-7 minutes. Remove the tofu from the skillet and set aside.

- In the same skillet, add sesame oil. Add minced garlic and grated ginger, and sauté for 1 minute until fragrant.

- Add sliced bell peppers, snow peas, mushrooms, and julienned carrots to the skillet. Stir-fry for 5-6 minutes until the vegetables are tender-crisp.

- Return the cooked tofu to the skillet. Pour the sauce over the tofu and vegetables. Stir well to coat everything evenly. Cook for an additional 2-3 minutes until the sauce thickens.

- Garnish with chopped green onions and sesame seeds if desired.

- Serve the vegetable stir-fry hot over cooked rice or noodles, if using.

Lemon Garlic Shrimp Scampi with Zucchini Noodles

Main dishes

Cook time:
10 min

Prep time:
15 min

Servings:
4

Ingredients:

- 1 pound (450g) large shrimp, peeled and deveined
- 4 medium zucchini
- 4 tablespoons (60ml) olive oil, divided
- 4 cloves garlic, minced
- 1/4 cup (60ml) fresh lemon juice
- Zest of 1 lemon
- 1/4 cup (15g) chopped fresh parsley
- Salt and pepper to taste
- Red pepper flakes (optional)
- Grated Parmesan cheese (optional)

Directions:

- Using a spiralizer, spiralize the zucchini into noodles. Set aside.

- Heat 2 tablespoons of olive oil in a large skillet over medium-high heat. Add the shrimp and cook for 2-3 minutes on each side until pink and opaque. Remove the shrimp from the skillet and set aside.

- In the same skillet, add the remaining 2 tablespoons of olive oil. Add the minced garlic and cook for 1 minute until fragrant.

- Add the zucchini noodles to the skillet and toss to coat in the garlic-infused oil. Cook for 2-3 minutes until the noodles are tender but still slightly crisp.

- Return the cooked shrimp to the skillet. Add fresh lemon juice, lemon zest, chopped parsley, salt, pepper, and red pepper flakes if desired. Toss everything together until well combined and heated through, about 1-2 minutes.

- Serve the lemon garlic shrimp scampi with zucchini noodles immediately. Optionally, sprinkle with grated Parmesan cheese before serving.

Nutritional Value (Per Serving):

- Calories: Approximately 250 kcal
- Fat: 14g
- Cholesterol: 170mg
- Sodium: 310mg
- Carbohydrates: 7g
- Protein: 24g

Eggplant Parmesan with Gluten-Free Bread Crumbs

Main dishes

Cook time:
45 min

Prep time:
20 min

Servings:
4

Ingredients:

For the Eggplant:
- 1 large eggplant, sliced into 1/2-inch rounds
- 2 eggs, beaten
- 1 cup (120g) gluten-free bread crumbs
- 1/2 cup (60g) grated Parmesan cheese (ensure it's gluten-free)
- 1 teaspoon (5ml) dried oregano
- 1 teaspoon (5ml) dried basil
- Salt and pepper to taste
- Olive oil, for frying

For the Assembly:
- 2 cups (480ml) gluten-free marinara sauce
- 1 cup (120g) shredded mozzarella cheese (ensure it's gluten-free)
- Fresh basil leaves, for garnish

Nutritional Value (Per Serving):

- Calories: Approximately 380 kcal
- Fat: 18g
- Cholesterol: 110mg
- Sodium: 900mg
- Carbohydrates: 35g
- Protein: 20g

Directions:

- Preheat the oven to 375°F (190°C). Lightly grease a baking sheet with olive oil.

- In a shallow dish, combine the gluten-free bread crumbs, grated Parmesan cheese, dried oregano, dried basil, salt, and pepper.

- Dip each eggplant slice into the beaten eggs, then dredge in the bread crumb mixture, ensuring each slice is evenly coated.

- Heat a generous amount of olive oil in a large skillet over medium heat. Fry the coated eggplant slices in batches until golden brown and crispy on both sides, about 3-4 minutes per side. Transfer the cooked eggplant slices to a paper towel-lined plate to drain excess oil.

- In a separate bowl, mix the shredded mozzarella cheese with the marinara sauce.

- Arrange half of the fried eggplant slices in a single layer on the prepared baking sheet. Spoon half of the marinara and cheese mixture over the eggplant slices.

- Layer the remaining eggplant slices on top and cover with the remaining marinara and cheese mixture.

- Bake in the preheated oven for 20-25 minutes, or until the cheese is melted and bubbly.

- Garnish with fresh basil leaves before serving.

Mexican Stuffed Sweet Potatoes with Black Beans and Salsa

 Main dishes

 Cook time:
1 hr

 Prep time:
15 min

 Servings:
4

Ingredients:

- 4 medium-sized sweet potatoes
- 1 can (15 oz / 425g) black beans, drained and rinsed
- 1 cup (240ml) salsa
- 1 avocado, diced
- 1/2 cup (60g) shredded cheddar cheese (optional)
- Fresh cilantro leaves, for garnish
- Salt and pepper to taste

Nutritional Value (Per Serving):

- Calories: Approximately 320 kcal
- Fat: 8g
- Cholesterol: 0mg
- Sodium: 640mg
- Carbohydrates: 53g
- Protein: 10g

Directions:

- Preheat the oven to 400°F (200°C). Line a baking sheet with parchment paper.

- Scrub the sweet potatoes clean and pierce each one several times with a fork. Place them on the prepared baking sheet and bake for 45-60 minutes, or until tender when pierced with a fork.

- While the sweet potatoes are baking, prepare the filling. In a medium saucepan, heat the black beans over medium heat until warmed through. Season with salt and pepper to taste.

- Once the sweet potatoes are cooked, remove them from the oven and let them cool slightly.

- Slice each sweet potato lengthwise and fluff the flesh with a fork.

- Divide the warm black beans evenly among the sweet potatoes, spooning them over the fluffed flesh.

- Top each stuffed sweet potato with salsa, diced avocado, and shredded cheddar cheese, if using.

- Garnish with fresh cilantro leaves and serve immediately.

Baked Honey Mustard Glazed Salmon with Roasted Brussels Sprouts

Main dishes

Cook time:
25 min

Prep time:
10 min

Servings:
4

Ingredients:

For the Salmon:
- 4 salmon fillets (about 6 oz / 170g each)
- 1/4 cup (60ml) honey
- 2 tablespoons (30ml) whole grain mustard
- 1 tablespoon (15ml) olive oil
- 1 tablespoon (15ml) lemon juice
- Salt and pepper to taste

For the Brussels Sprouts:
- 1 pound (450g) Brussels sprouts, trimmed and halved
- 2 tablespoons (30ml) olive oil
- Salt and pepper to taste

Directions:

- Preheat the oven to 400°F (200°C). Line a baking sheet with parchment paper.

- In a small bowl, whisk together the honey, mustard, olive oil, lemon juice, salt, and pepper to make the glaze.

- Place the salmon fillets on the prepared baking sheet. Brush the glaze generously over the tops of the salmon fillets.

- In a large bowl, toss the Brussels sprouts with olive oil, salt, and pepper until evenly coated.

- Arrange the Brussels sprouts around the salmon on the baking sheet.

- Bake in the preheated oven for 15-20 minutes, or until the salmon is cooked through and flakes easily with a fork, and the Brussels sprouts are tender and caramelized.

- Remove from the oven and let rest for a few minutes before serving.

Nutritional Value (Per Serving):

- Calories: Approximately 380 kcal
- Fat: 18g
- Cholesterol: 75mg
- Sodium: 290mg
- Carbohydrates: 23g
- Protein: 32g

Snack Recipes

Guacamole with Vegetable Sticks

Snack

Cook time:
0 min

Prep time:
10 min

Servings:
4

Ingredients:

- 2 ripe avocados
- 1 small tomato, diced
- 1/4 cup (15g) finely chopped red onion
- 1/4 cup (15g) chopped fresh cilantro
- 1 jalapeño pepper, seeded and minced (optional)
- Juice of 1 lime
- Salt and pepper, to taste
- 2 medium carrots, cut into sticks
- 2 medium cucumbers, cut into sticks
- 2 bell peppers (assorted colors), cut into sticks

Directions:

- Cut the avocados in half, remove the pits, and scoop the flesh into a mixing bowl.

- Mash the avocados using a fork until smooth but still slightly chunky.

- Add the diced tomato, finely chopped red onion, chopped cilantro, minced jalapeño pepper (if using), and lime juice to the mashed avocado. Mix well to combine.

- Season the guacamole with salt and pepper according to taste.

- Prepare the vegetable sticks by cutting the carrots, cucumbers, and bell peppers into sticks.

- Serve the guacamole in a bowl alongside the vegetable sticks.

Nutritional Value (Per Serving):

- Calories: Approximately 170 kcal
- Fat: 13g
- Cholesterol: 0mg
- Sodium: 210mg
- Carbohydrates: 15g
- Protein: 3g

Trail Mix with Nuts, Seeds, and Dried Fruits

Snack

Cook time:
0 min

Prep time:
5 min

Servings:
8

Ingredients:

- 1 cup (150g) almonds
- 1 cup (150g) cashews
- 1 cup (150g) pumpkin seeds
- 1 cup (150g) sunflower seeds
- 1 cup (150g) dried cranberries
- 1 cup (150g) raisins
- 1/2 cup (75g) dried apricots, chopped
- 1/2 cup (75g) dried mango, chopped

Directions:

- In a large mixing bowl, combine the almonds, cashews, pumpkin seeds, sunflower seeds, dried cranberries, raisins, chopped dried apricots, and chopped dried mango.

- Toss the ingredients together until well mixed.

- Transfer the trail mix to an airtight container or portion into individual snack bags for convenience.

- Store in a cool, dry place until ready to enjoy.

Nutritional Value (Per Serving):

- Calories: Approximately 320 kcal
- Fat: 18g
- Cholesterol: 0mg
- Sodium: 5mg
- Carbohydrates: 35g
- Protein: 10g

Deviled Eggs with Dill and Paprika

Snack

Cook time:
10 min

Prep time:
20 min

Servings:
6

Ingredients:

- 6 large eggs
- 1/4 cup (60g) mayonnaise
- 1 teaspoon (5ml) Dijon mustard
- 1 tablespoon (15ml) fresh dill, finely chopped
- 1/2 teaspoon (2.5ml) white vinegar
- Salt and pepper, to taste
- Paprika, for garnish

Directions:

- Place the eggs in a single layer in a saucepan and cover with water. Bring to a boil over medium-high heat. Once boiling, remove from heat, cover, and let sit for 10 minutes.

- While the eggs are cooking, prepare a bowl of ice water. Once the eggs are done, transfer them to the ice water bath to cool for a few minutes.

- Once cooled, peel the eggs and slice them in half lengthwise. Carefully remove the yolks and place them in a separate bowl.

- Mash the egg yolks with a fork until they are crumbly. Add mayonnaise, Dijon mustard, chopped dill, white vinegar, salt, and pepper. Mix until well combined and creamy.

- Spoon or pipe the yolk mixture back into the egg white halves.

- Sprinkle the deviled eggs with paprika for garnish.

- Refrigerate the deviled eggs for at least 30 minutes before serving to allow the flavors to meld.

Nutritional Value (Per Serving):

- Calories: Approximately 130 kcal
- Fat: 11g
- Cholesterol: 215mg
- Sodium: 150mg
- Carbohydrates: 1g
- Protein: 6g

Hummus with Gluten-Free Crackers or Veggie Chips

Snack

Cook time:
0 min

Prep time:
10 min

Servings:
6

Ingredients:

- 1 can (15 ounces / 425g) chickpeas, drained and rinsed
- 1/4 cup (60ml) tahini
- 2 cloves garlic, minced
- 3 tablespoons (45ml) lemon juice
- 2 tablespoons (30ml) extra virgin olive oil
- 1/2 teaspoon (2.5ml) ground cumin
- Salt, to taste
- Water, as needed
- Gluten-free crackers or veggie chips, for serving

Directions:

- In a food processor, combine the chickpeas, tahini, minced garlic, lemon juice, olive oil, ground cumin, and a pinch of salt.

- Process the mixture until smooth, scraping down the sides of the bowl as needed. If the hummus is too thick, add water, 1 tablespoon at a time, until it reaches your desired consistency.

- Taste the hummus and adjust the seasoning, adding more salt or lemon juice if necessary.

- Transfer the hummus to a serving bowl and drizzle with a little extra olive oil if desired. Serve with gluten-free crackers or veggie chips for dipping.

Nutritional Value (Per Serving):

- Calories: Approximately 180 kcal
- Fat: 11g
- Cholesterol: 0mg
- Sodium: 210mg
- Carbohydrates: 16g
- Protein: 5g

Cottage Cheese with Pineapple Chunks

Snack

Cook time:
0 min

Prep time:
5 min

Servings:
2

Ingredients:

- 1 cup (226g) cottage cheese
- 1 cup (165g) fresh pineapple chunks

Directions:

- In a bowl, scoop out the cottage cheese.

- Rinse the fresh pineapple under cold water and peel it. Cut the pineapple into bite-sized chunks.

- Add the pineapple chunks to the bowl of cottage cheese.

- Gently stir the cottage cheese and pineapple together until well combined.

- Divide the mixture evenly into serving bowls or plates.

- Serve immediately and enjoy!

Nutritional Value (Per Serving):

- Calories: Approximately 145 kcal
- Fat: 2g
- Cholesterol: 9mg
- Sodium: 390mg
- Carbohydrates: 17g
- Protein: 15g

Baked Sweet Potato Fries

Snack

Cook time:
25 min

Prep time:
10 min

Servings:
4

Ingredients:

- 2 large sweet potatoes (about 800g), washed and dried
- 2 tablespoons (30ml) olive oil
- 1 teaspoon (5g) garlic powder
- 1 teaspoon (5g) paprika
- 1/2 teaspoon (2.5g) salt
- 1/4 teaspoon (1.25g) black pepper
- **Optional:** chopped fresh parsley for garnish

Directions:

- Preheat your oven to 425°F (220°C) and line a baking sheet with parchment paper.

- Cut the sweet potatoes into evenly sized fries. Aim for about 1/4 inch (0.6 cm) thickness.

- In a large bowl, toss the sweet potato fries with olive oil, garlic powder, paprika, salt, and black pepper until evenly coated.

- Arrange the seasoned sweet potato fries in a single layer on the prepared baking sheet, making sure they are not overcrowded.

- Bake in the preheated oven for 20-25 minutes, flipping halfway through, until the fries are golden brown and crispy.

- Once done, remove the fries from the oven and let them cool slightly. Sprinkle with chopped fresh parsley if desired.

- Serve the baked sweet potato fries hot as a delicious and healthy side dish or snack.

Nutritional Value (Per Serving):

- Calories: Approximately 185 kcal
- Fat: 7g
- Cholesterol: 0mg
- Sodium: 318mg
- Carbohydrates: 29g
- Protein: 2g

Cheese and Grape Skewers

Snack

Cook time:
0 min

Prep time:
15 min

Servings:
4

Ingredients:

- 1 cup (150g) seedless grapes
- 4 ounces (115g) cheese (such as cheddar, gouda, or mozzarella), cut into cubes
- 8 skewers

Directions:

- Rinse the grapes and pat them dry with a paper towel.

- Prepare the cheese by cutting it into bite-sized cubes.

- Thread the grapes and cheese cubes alternately onto the skewers, leaving a little space at the end of each skewer for holding.

- Repeat the process until all the skewers are filled with grapes and cheese.

- Arrange the skewers on a serving platter and refrigerate until ready to serve.

- Serve the cheese and grape skewers as a delightful appetizer or snack at your next gathering.

Nutritional Value (Per Serving):

- Calories: Approximately 120 kcal
- Fat: 8g
- Cholesterol: 25mg
- Sodium: 200mg
- Carbohydrates: 8g
- Protein: 6g

Ants on a Log

Snack

Cook time:
0 min

Prep time:
10 min

Servings:
4

Ingredients:

- 4 celery stalks
- 1/4 cup (60g) peanut butter
- 1/4 cup (40g) raisins

Directions:

- Wash the celery stalks thoroughly and pat them dry with a paper towel. Trim off the ends of each stalk.

- Spread peanut butter generously along the center of each celery stalk, leaving about a quarter-inch border on each side.

- Arrange raisins on top of the peanut butter, pressing them gently into the spread.

- Repeat the process for each celery stalk until all are filled with peanut butter and raisins.

- Serve the "Ants on a Log" celery sticks on a plate or platter.

Nutritional Value (Per Serving):

- Calories: Approximately 110 kcal
- Fat: 7g
- Cholesterol: 0mg
- Sodium: 90mg
- Carbohydrates: 10g
- Protein: 4g

Dark Chocolate Covered Almonds

Snack

Cook time:
10 min

Prep time:
15 min

Servings:
8

Ingredients:

- 2 cups (280g) whole almonds
- 8 ounces (225g) dark chocolate chips or chopped dark chocolate
- 1 tablespoon (15ml) coconut oil

Directions:

- Line a baking sheet with parchment paper.

- In a double boiler or microwave-safe bowl, melt the dark chocolate and coconut oil together until smooth and well combined. Stir frequently to prevent burning if using a double boiler, or microwave in 30-second intervals, stirring between each interval.

- Once the chocolate is melted and smooth, remove it from the heat source.

- Add the almonds to the melted chocolate, stirring until all almonds are evenly coated.

- Using a fork or a slotted spoon, remove the chocolate-covered almonds from the bowl, allowing any excess chocolate to drip off, and place them on the prepared baking sheet, making sure they are not touching each other.

- Allow the chocolate-covered almonds to cool and set at room temperature for about 10-15 minutes or until the chocolate hardens.

- Once the chocolate has hardened, transfer the baking sheet to the refrigerator for an additional 10-15 minutes to speed up the setting process.

- Once fully set, transfer the dark chocolate covered almonds to an airtight container for storage or serve immediately.

Nutritional Value (Per Serving):

- Calories: Approximately 250 kcal
- Fat: 18g
- Cholesterol: 0mg
- Sodium: 0mg
- Carbohydrates: 17g
- Protein: 6g

Roasted Chickpeas with Seasonings

Snack

Cook time:
40 min

Prep time:
5 min

Servings:
4

Ingredients:

- 2 cans (15 ounces each, about 425g) chickpeas (garbanzo beans), drained and rinsed
- 2 tablespoons (30ml) olive oil
- 1 teaspoon (5ml) paprika
- 1 teaspoon (5ml) ground cumin
- 1/2 teaspoon (2.5ml) garlic powder
- 1/2 teaspoon (2.5ml) onion powder
- 1/2 teaspoon (2.5ml) salt
- 1/4 teaspoon (1.25ml) black pepper

Directions:

- Preheat your oven to 400°F (200°C). Line a baking sheet with parchment paper or aluminum foil for easy cleanup.

- Pat the drained and rinsed chickpeas dry with paper towels or a clean kitchen towel. Remove any loose skins that come off.

- In a large bowl, toss the chickpeas with olive oil until they are evenly coated.

- In a small bowl, mix together the paprika, ground cumin, garlic powder, onion powder, salt, and black pepper.

- Sprinkle the seasoning mixture over the chickpeas and toss until they are well coated with the spices.

- Spread the seasoned chickpeas in a single layer on the prepared baking sheet.

- Roast the chickpeas in the preheated oven for 30-40 minutes, stirring halfway through the cooking time, until they are golden brown and crispy.

- Once roasted, remove the chickpeas from the oven and let them cool slightly before serving.

Nutritional Value (Per Serving):

- Calories: Approximately 220 kcal
- Fat: 8g
- Cholesterol: 0mg
- Sodium: 390mg
- Carbohydrates: 28g
- Protein: 9g

Chapter 6: Frequently Asked Questions (FAQs)

What Grains are Gluten-Free?

Several grains are naturally free from gluten and can be safely consumed by individuals following a gluten-free diet. Here are some common gluten-free grains:

- **Rice:** Rice is a versatile gluten-free grain that comes in various forms, including white rice, brown rice, jasmine rice, and basmati rice. It can be used as a side dish, in salads, soups, stir-fries, and even desserts.

- **Quinoa:** Quinoa is a nutritious gluten-free grain that is high in protein, fiber, and essential nutrients. It has a nutty flavor and a slightly chewy texture, making it a popular choice for salads, pilafs, and breakfast porridge.

- **Corn (Maize):** Corn is a gluten-free grain that is widely used in both its whole form and as cornmeal or corn flour. It can be incorporated into dishes such as corn tortillas, polenta, cornbread, and popcorn.

- **Buckwheat:** Despite its name, buckwheat is not related to wheat and is naturally gluten-free. It is commonly used in the form of buckwheat groats, flour, and noodles in dishes like porridge, pancakes, and soba noodles.

- **Millet:** Millet is a gluten-free grain that is rich in nutrients like magnesium, phosphorus, and antioxidants. It has a mild, slightly sweet flavor and can be cooked and used in place of rice or added to salads, pilafs, and baked goods.

- **Sorghum:** Sorghum is a gluten-free grain that is drought-resistant and widely cultivated in many parts of the world. It has a mild flavor and can be used in a variety of dishes, including soups, stews, salads, and gluten-free baked goods.

- **Amaranth:** Amaranth is a gluten-free pseudo-grain that is rich in protein, fiber, and micronutrients. It has a slightly peppery flavor and a sticky texture when cooked, making it suitable for porridge, soups, and baked goods.

- **Teff:** Teff is a gluten-free grain native to Ethiopia and Eritrea, where it is commonly used to make injera, a traditional flatbread. It has a slightly nutty flavor and can be used in porridge, baked goods, and as a gluten-free flour alternative.

These gluten-free grains provide a diverse range of flavors, textures, and nutritional benefits, making them valuable staples in a gluten-free diet. Incorporating a variety of gluten-free grains into your meals ensures a balanced and satisfying diet while adhering to gluten-free dietary restrictions.

Is gluten-free the same as wheat-free?

While gluten-free and wheat-free diets share some similarities, they are not the same. Here's a breakdown of the differences between gluten-free and wheat-free diets:

Gluten-Free Diet: A gluten-free diet excludes all sources of gluten, a protein found in wheat, barley, rye, and their derivatives. This means avoiding foods such as bread, pasta, baked goods, cereals, beer, and certain sauces and condiments that contain gluten-containing ingredients or are at risk of cross-contamination with gluten.

In addition to wheat, gluten-free diets also exclude barley and rye, as these grains contain gluten. Individuals with celiac disease, non-celiac gluten sensitivity, or wheat allergies typically follow a gluten-free diet to manage their condition and prevent adverse reactions to gluten.

Gluten-free foods include naturally gluten-free grains like rice, quinoa, corn, and buckwheat, as well as gluten-free alternatives such as gluten-free bread, pasta, and baked goods made from alternative flours like almond flour, coconut flour, or chickpea flour.

Wheat-Free Diet: A wheat-free diet eliminates wheat and wheat-derived ingredients but may still include other sources of gluten such as barley and rye. Individuals with wheat allergies or sensitivities may follow a wheat-free diet to avoid adverse reactions to wheat proteins.

While wheat is a primary source of gluten, not all gluten-containing grains are wheat-based. Barley and rye also contain gluten, so a wheat-free diet does not necessarily eliminate gluten entirely. Individuals following a wheat-free diet need to be cautious about consuming products made with barley or rye, as well as foods that may contain hidden sources of wheat.

Wheat-free foods may include gluten-containing grains like barley and rye, as well as gluten-free grains like rice, quinoa, and corn. However, individuals on a wheat-free diet must carefully read labels and ingredients lists to avoid wheat-derived ingredients in processed foods and food products.

In summary, while both gluten-free and wheat-free diets involve avoiding certain grains, gluten-free diets exclude all sources of gluten, including wheat, barley, and rye, whereas wheat-free diets only eliminate wheat and wheat-derived ingredients, allowing for the inclusion of other gluten-containing grains. It's important for individuals following these diets to understand their specific dietary restrictions and choose foods accordingly to ensure safe and healthy eating.

Can I Drink Beer on a Gluten-Free Diet?

Beer is typically made from gluten-containing grains such as barley, wheat, and rye, which means that most traditional beers are not suitable for individuals following a gluten-free diet. However, in recent years, there has been an increase in the availability of gluten-free beers made from alternative grains or processed to remove gluten. Here's what you need to know about drinking beer on a gluten-free diet:

Traditional Beer Contains Gluten: Most traditional beers are brewed using barley, wheat, or rye, all of which contain gluten. During the brewing process, gluten proteins are extracted from these grains and remain present in the final product, making traditional beer unsafe for individuals with celiac disease or gluten sensitivity.

Gluten-Free Beers: Fortunately, there are now gluten-free beers available that are made from gluten-free grains such as sorghum, rice, millet, buckwheat, or corn. These beers are specially formulated to be gluten-free and safe for individuals with gluten-related disorders.

Check Labels and Certifications: When choosing gluten-free beer, it's essential to read labels carefully and look for products that are labeled as "gluten-free" or certified gluten-free by reputable organizations. This ensures that the beer has undergone testing to verify that it meets gluten-free standards and contains less than 20 parts per million (ppm) of gluten, the threshold considered safe for most individuals with celiac disease.

Avoid Cross-Contamination: While gluten-free beers are made without gluten-containing grains, there is still a risk of cross-contamination during the brewing process or from shared equipment. To minimize this risk, choose beers from dedicated gluten-free breweries or those with stringent gluten-free protocols in place.

Explore Gluten-Removed Beers: Some beers labeled as "gluten-removed" or "crafted to remove gluten" undergo a process to reduce gluten levels after brewing. However, the safety of these beers for individuals with celiac disease or gluten sensitivity is a subject of debate within the medical community. Some individuals may tolerate gluten-removed beers well, while others may experience adverse reactions. It's essential to consult with a healthcare professional before consuming gluten-removed beers, especially if you have celiac disease.

Consider Gluten-Free Alternatives: If you're unable to find safe gluten-free beers or prefer to avoid the potential risks associated with gluten-removed beers, consider exploring other gluten-free alcoholic beverages such as cider, wine, distilled spirits, or cocktails made with gluten-free ingredients.

In conclusion, while traditional beers are not suitable for individuals following a gluten-free diet, there are gluten-free beer options available that can be enjoyed safely. By checking labels, choosing certified gluten-free products, and being mindful of potential cross-contamination, you can indulge in a refreshing beer without compromising your gluten-free lifestyle.

How Long Does It Take to Feel the Benefits of a Gluten-Free Diet?

The timeline for experiencing the benefits of a gluten-free diet can vary greatly from person to person and depends on several factors, including the individual's underlying health condition, the severity of gluten-related symptoms, and adherence to the gluten-free diet. Here's what to consider:

Immediate Relief of Symptoms: Some individuals may experience immediate relief from certain symptoms shortly after eliminating gluten from their diet. This can include improvements in gastrointestinal issues such as bloating, gas, diarrhea, and abdominal pain, as well as reductions in fatigue, brain fog, and skin problems like dermatitis herpetiformis.

Short-Term Benefits: Within the first few weeks of starting a gluten-free diet, many people notice significant improvements in their overall well-being and quality of life. Digestive symptoms often improve, energy levels may increase, and mental clarity may improve. Individuals with conditions like celiac disease may also experience healing of the intestinal lining and resolution of inflammation within a few weeks to months.

Long-Term Benefits: Over time, adhering to a gluten-free diet can lead to sustained improvements in health and symptom management for individuals with gluten-related disorders such as celiac disease or non-celiac gluten sensitivity. Long-term benefits may include reduced risk of complications associated with untreated celiac disease, such as nutrient deficiencies, osteoporosis, infertility, and certain autoimmune diseases.

Individual Variability: It's important to recognize that the timeline for experiencing benefits on a gluten-free diet can vary widely among individuals. While some people may notice significant improvements within days or weeks, others may require several months or even years to fully recover from the effects of gluten-related disorders and regain optimal health.

Commitment to Adherence: The degree of adherence to a gluten-free diet also plays a crucial role in determining the timeline for experiencing benefits. Strict adherence to the diet, including avoiding hidden sources of gluten and preventing cross-contamination, is essential for maximizing the effectiveness of the gluten-free approach and achieving optimal outcomes.

Consultation with Healthcare Providers: Individuals experiencing persistent symptoms or complications despite following a gluten-free diet should consult with healthcare providers, including gastroenterologists, dietitians, and other specialists, for comprehensive evaluation and management. Additional testing, dietary modifications, and personalized treatment strategies may be necessary to address underlying health concerns and optimize outcomes.

In summary, the timeline for feeling the benefits of a gluten-free diet varies depending on individual factors, including the specific health condition, symptom severity, adherence to the diet, and overall health status. While some people may experience immediate relief of symptoms, others may require more time to fully reap the benefits of eliminating gluten from their diet. It's essential to stay committed to the gluten-free lifestyle and seek guidance from healthcare providers for personalized support and management.

Chapter 7: Resources and References

Recommended Reading

If you're seeking authoritative information on gluten-free living from scientific and government organizations, consider exploring publications and resources provided by the following institutions:

National Institutes of Health (NIH): The NIH offers a wealth of information on celiac disease, gluten sensitivity, and gluten-related research through its National Institute of Diabetes and Digestive and Kidney Diseases (NIDDK). Visit the NIDDK website for up-to-date publications, clinical guidelines, and research findings related to gluten-related disorders.

Centers for Disease Control and Prevention (CDC): The CDC provides valuable resources on celiac disease and gluten-related disorders, including prevalence data, diagnostic guidelines, and educational materials for healthcare professionals and the general public. Explore the CDC's website for authoritative information on gluten-related health issues.

World Health Organization (WHO): The WHO offers global perspectives on celiac disease and gluten-related disorders, including epidemiological data, public health strategies, and recommendations for diagnosis and management. Access WHO publications and reports for comprehensive insights into gluten-related health concerns.

U.S. Department of Agriculture (USDA): The USDA's Food and Nutrition Information Center (FNIC) provides evidence-based nutrition information, including resources on gluten-free diets, food labeling regulations, and dietary guidelines for individuals with celiac disease or gluten intolerance. Explore the FNIC website for reliable nutrition guidance.

European Food Safety Authority (EFSA): The EFSA assesses scientific research on food safety and provides recommendations on gluten-related issues, including gluten intake thresholds, labeling requirements, and risk assessments for gluten-sensitive individuals. Visit the EFSA website for authoritative guidance on gluten-related topics.

National Health Service (NHS): The NHS in the United Kingdom offers practical advice and support for individuals with celiac disease and gluten intolerance through its website. Access information on gluten-free diets, diagnosis, treatment, and ongoing management of gluten-related conditions.

Coeliac UK: While not a government organization, Coeliac UK is a leading charity in the UK dedicated to supporting individuals with celiac disease and promoting gluten-free living. Their website offers a wealth of resources, including practical guides, recipes, and community support for those following a gluten-free diet.

By exploring publications and resources from these scientific and government organizations, you can access reliable and evidence-based information on gluten-related health concerns, dietary recommendations, and strategies for gluten-free living. Stay informed and empowered to make informed decisions about your gluten-free lifestyle with guidance from these authoritative sources.

Apps

In addition to books, there are many apps that can serve as valuable resources for your gluten-free journey. Here are some trusted and apps to explore:

App	Platform	Features
Fooducate	Android iOS	• Provides gluten-free recipe ideas. • Helps you learn about the overall nutritional content of foods. • Allows you to search for gluten-free versions of popular products. • Includes a community forum for tips and discussions. • Offers a food tracker and daily diet tips.
Mealime	Android iOS	• Offers meal plans and recipes • Helps you plan gluten-free meals • Great for creating shopping lists
mySymptoms	Android iOS	• Acts as a food diary • Helps you track symptoms related to your diet • Useful for identifying which foods you can and can't eat
Find Me Gluten Free	Android iOS	• Locates gluten-free restaurants nearby. • Provides user reviews and ratings. • Helps you find safe dining options
Yummly Recipes	Android iOS	• Offers a wide range of cooking recipes • Allows you to filter for gluten-free options • Includes a shopping list feature
Fit Men Cook	Android iOS	• Provides healthy recipes and meal planning • Includes gluten-free options
AllergyEats	Android iOS	• Focuses on allergies and dietary restrictions. • Helps you find allergy-friendly restaurants. • Useful for those with gluten sensitivity
Gluten Free Scanner	Android iOS	• Scan barcodes of food products to check if they are gluten-free

Remember that the best app for you depends on your specific needs and preferences. Feel free to explore these options and choose the one that aligns with your gluten-free journey.

Conclusion

Embarking on a gluten-free journey is not just a dietary change but a transformative lifestyle shift that can have profound effects on your health and well-being. Throughout this book, we've explored the fundamentals of living gluten-free, from understanding gluten and its implications to practical tips for grocery shopping, meal planning, and dining out.

By adopting a gluten-free diet, you've taken a proactive step towards managing gluten-related conditions such as celiac disease, gluten sensitivity, or wheat allergies. Whether you're newly diagnosed or exploring gluten-free living for health reasons, you've demonstrated resilience, adaptability, and a commitment to prioritizing your health.

Remember that transitioning to a gluten-free lifestyle may come with its challenges, but with patience, perseverance, and support from healthcare professionals, family, and friends, you can navigate the journey successfully. Celebrate the victories, no matter how small, and be kind to yourself as you adjust to this new way of eating and living.

As you continue on your gluten-free journey, stay informed, stay connected, and stay empowered. Seek out reliable resources, engage with online communities, and explore new recipes and culinary experiences that enrich your gluten-free lifestyle. Embrace the opportunity to discover delicious gluten-free alternatives, experiment with new flavors, and nourish your body with wholesome, nutritious foods.

Above all, remember that living gluten-free is not just about dietary restrictions—it's about embracing a lifestyle of wellness, vitality, and self-care. Listen to your body, honor your dietary needs, and savor the joys of nourishing yourself with foods that make you feel good from the inside out.

Here's to your health, happiness, and the limitless possibilities of gluten-free living. May your journey be filled with delicious discoveries, vibrant health, and a renewed sense of vitality.

Bon appétit and cheers to your gluten-free adventure!

Appendices

Glossary of Gluten-Free Terms

Here are some key terms and phrases frequently used in the context of a gluten-free diet:

Gluten: A family of proteins found in wheat, barley, rye, and their derivatives, which can trigger adverse reactions in individuals with celiac disease, gluten sensitivity, or wheat allergies.

Celiac Disease: An autoimmune disorder characterized by a severe reaction to gluten consumption, resulting in damage to the lining of the small intestine and impairing nutrient absorption.

Gluten Sensitivity: A non-celiac condition in which individuals experience adverse symptoms upon gluten ingestion, without evidence of celiac disease or wheat allergy.

Wheat Allergy: An immune-mediated reaction to proteins found in wheat, resulting in symptoms such as hives, swelling, difficulty breathing, and gastrointestinal distress.

Cross-Contamination: The inadvertent transfer of gluten from gluten-containing foods to gluten-free foods or surfaces, posing a risk of gluten exposure for individuals following a gluten-free diet.

Gluten-Free Diet: A dietary regimen that excludes all sources of gluten, including wheat, barley, rye, and their derivatives, to manage gluten-related disorders and promote overall health.

Gluten-Free Certification: A designation indicating that a product has undergone testing to ensure compliance with gluten-free standards and contains less than 20 parts per million (ppm) of gluten.

Gluten-Free Alternatives: Ingredients and products that serve as substitutes for gluten-containing foods, such as gluten-free flours, grains, bread, pasta, and baked goods.

Gluten-Free Labeling: The practice of labeling food products as "gluten-free" to indicate that they are safe for individuals with celiac disease, gluten sensitivity, or wheat allergies to consume.

Hidden Gluten: Gluten-containing ingredients that may be present in processed foods, sauces, condiments, and additives under different names, making them difficult to identify without careful label reading.

Gluten-Free Cooking: The practice of preparing meals and recipes using gluten-free ingredients and cooking methods to accommodate individuals with gluten-related disorders.

Gluten-Free Dining: The process of selecting and enjoying meals at restaurants, cafes, and social gatherings while adhering to a gluten-free diet and avoiding gluten cross-contamination.

Gluten-Free Resources: Tools, organizations, websites, and apps that provide information, support, and resources for individuals following a gluten-free lifestyle.

Gluten-Free Community: A network of individuals, support groups, and online forums dedicated to sharing experiences, advice, and resources related to living gluten-free.

Gluten-Free Wellness: A holistic approach to gluten-free living that emphasizes nourishing the body with nutritious, whole foods, promoting physical and emotional well-being, and embracing a balanced lifestyle.

Measurement Conversion Charts

Conversion charts can be invaluable when working with recipes or dietary guidelines that use different measurement systems. Here are some common measurement conversions to help you navigate your gluten-free diet with ease:

Volume Conversions:

- 1 tablespoon (tbsp) = 3 teaspoons (tsp)
- 1 fluid ounce (fl oz) = 2 tablespoons
- 1 cup = 8 fluid ounces
- 1 pint (pt) = 2 cups
- 1 quart (qt) = 4 cups
- 1 gallon (gal) = 4 quarts

Weight Conversions:

- 1 ounce (oz) = 28.35 grams (g)
- 1 pound (lb) = 16 ounces
- 1 kilogram (kg) = 2.205 pounds

Metric to Imperial Conversions:

- 1 milliliter (ml) = 0.034 fluid ounces
- 1 liter (L) = 1.76 pints
- 1 gram (g) = 0.035 ounces
- 1 kilogram (kg) = 2.2 pounds

Temperature Conversions:

- Fahrenheit (°F) to Celsius (°C): (°F - 32) × 5/9
- Celsius (°C) to Fahrenheit (°F): (°C × 9/5) + 32

Oven Temperature Conversions:

- Very slow oven (250°F or 120°C)
- Slow oven (300°F or 150°C)
- Moderate oven (350°F or 180°C)
- Moderately hot oven (375°F or 190°C)
- Hot oven (400°F or 200°C)
- Very hot oven (450°F or 230°C)

Teaspoon to Milliliter (tsp to ml) Conversion:

- 1 teaspoon (tsp) = 5 milliliters (ml)

Tablespoon to Milliliter (tbsp to ml) Conversion:

- 1 tablespoon (tbsp) = 15 milliliters (ml)

Cup to Milliliter (cup to ml) Conversion:

- 1 cup = 240 milliliters (ml)

These conversion charts can be handy references when you come across recipes or dietary guidelines using different measurements. Whether you're following a recipe from a different region or converting nutrition labels, these charts will help ensure accurate and consistent measurements for your gluten-free diet.

Made in the USA
Columbia, SC
11 December 2024

49005385R00059